Medical
Partnership
Practice

Medical Partnership Practice

By Horace Cotton
&
Carlyle Grady, M.D.
Robert C. Hopkins, M.D.
Dale Wickham, M.D.
Fred L. Evans, M.D.
Bertram B. Moss, M.D.
Walter Sage Ravenal, M.D.
Emory Lipman George, M.D.

Medical Economics Book Division, Inc., Oradell, New Jersey

Sixth printing 1971

Contents

Foreword

Ten years ago, about one-sixth of all private physicians in the U.S. practiced in partnerships or groups. Since then, the proportion has zoomed to about one-third, with at least another one-sixth working together in less formal expense-sharing arrangements.

Judging from the many inquiries about combined practice received by MEDICAL ECONOMICS magazine, the next decade will see another sharp rise. For younger doctors especially, the clinical and financial advantages of combined practice seem often to outweigh its drawbacks.

Three-quarters of all the private physicians now in partnerships or groups are members of two- to five-man teams. And it's about the organization and operation of combined practices of this size that the doctors who query MEDICAL ECONOMICS most often want to know. They ask such specific questions as:

"How can I judge my chances of success if I team up with a colleague?" . . . "What are the tax advantages of partnership practice?" . . . "What are the best income-sharing arrangements?" . . . "As partners, should we insure each other's lives?" . . . "How should I handle my current accounts receivable if I enter a partnership?" . . . "What are the customary fringe benefits of partnership practice?"

This book answers those questions and many more.

The 11 chapters of Part I, written by management consultant Horace Cotton, give practical advice on establishing and operating a small partnership. This material first appeared as a series of articles in MEDICAL ECONOMICS.

Mr. Cotton spent eight years at Oxford and a year at Duke University. He has had broad experience as a hospital administrator, biostatistician and research analyst.

In the early 1950s, he founded the professional management firm known now as PM Southeast, Inc. Within seven years he had built this into an organization serving 500 physicians in six states. As a management consultant, he helped organize more than 100 medical partnerships—and helped take a dozen apart.

In 1960 Mr. Cotton joined the staff of MEDICAL ECONOMICS as Executive Editor. In 1961 he became Contributing Editor, in order to devote more time to writing. One result has been "Aid for the Doctor's Aide," his definitive book for medical office assistants, published by Medical Economics Book Division, Inc.

Part II of the present book supplements Mr. Cotton's advice with seven chapters in which seven doctors give personal accounts of their experience in combined practice. This material also appeared originally in MEDICAL ECONOMICS.

Besides illustrating many of the points made in the first 11 chapters, Part II describes some practice variations that anyone contemplating partnership might well consider. The authors are diversified not only in experience, but also in specialty and geographical location. They range from a man starting practice to another with 20 years' service. Two are located in the East, one is on the West Coast, the rest are in the Midwest. One is an internist, one is a pediatrician, one specializes in obstetrics, and the others are general practitioners.

If you're at all interested in partnership practice, you'll find this a uniquely helpful book. Personally, I learned a lot from it.

April 15, 1964

William Alan Richardson, Editorial Director
MEDICAL ECONOMICS, Oradell, N.J.

Part I

By Horace Cotton
A management consultant who has helped
organize more than 100 medical partnerships—and
helped take a dozen apart—talks
frankly about the things that make partners
succeed or fail.

1.

The pros and cons of partnership

I know more than 1,000 physicians who are practicing in partnerships. Some—a minority—work in clusters of 10 or more. Most
of them work in pairs, though a good percentage work in trios
and quartets. Over the years, I've helped put together more than
100 of their partnerships, and a dozen times I've had to lend a
hand in taking them apart. In these processes I've learned that
unexpected things can happen when doctors team up.

I've discovered that the most unlikely looking combinations
can succeed triumphantly. You might think, for example, that
a 45-year age difference between two G.P.s would stand in the
way of a successful partnership. But I helped start up a two-man
team when one partner was 73 and the other 28. No, they weren't
kin. They worked in perfect harmony for seven years. At 80, as
planned, the old man retired.

How many male pediatricians would go straight from residency into a junior partnership with a woman who didn't even start her medical studies until she was past 40? I know one who did. And he's glad. Not just because he now owns half of the best children's practice in a good-sized city. As he'll tell you: "I have the joy of working alongside one of the finest human beings a man could hope to meet."

Contrariwise, you might suppose that two boyhood friends—inseparable through high school, college, medical school and interneship—would have it made when they launched a joint practice. Yet one of the most distasteful jobs I ever had was keeping this David-and-Jonathan pair from working mayhem on each other.

Do close ties of blood or marriage provide a sounder base for a professional partnership? Father-and-son combinations can work out well, but I've seen partner-brothers fail miserably. And of the five husband-wife teams I've known, four are successes. The fifth couple finally called all bets off—including the marital one.

Most management consultants could delve into their files and come up with case histories like those I've briefly mentioned. That's because advising doctors on partnerships takes up a good deal of the modern consultant's working time. Combined practice is becoming increasingly popular every year, and already five out of 10 self-employed U.S. physicians have linked up with others in one way or another. How closely? All the way from loose, informal expense-sharing arrangements to tightly organized group practices. But the favorite link is the small partnership, in which two or three physicians pool incomes and expenses and then share the profits in agreed proportions.

If you're not now in such a partnership, you've probably wondered more than once: "Am I missing the boat?" Yes, I think you may be, and I'll tell you why. But first let me flash you a few warning signals:

Some men are born loners and should stay that way. I mean the doctors who do their best work by themselves. You may be one of them. See if you're anything like a surgeon I once knew—a man I'll call Alfred Bush.

When I met him, Dr. Bush was dissolving his third partnership. He told me despondently: "I have a genius for picking the wrong man. My first partner wanted to do surgery beyond his ability. No. 2 was money-mad. Now No. 3 insists on a vote whenever we buy paper clips."

When I talked things over with No. 3, though, I got another story. According to him, the first partner had no desire to practice beyond his competence; he'd rebelled against Dr. Bush's habit of appropriating all major surgery to himself. The second partner had suggested revision of some fees that Dr. Bush had been charging for many years. "As for me," said the third partner, "I'm fed up with his way of making all decisions on his own. For instance, I didn't even know he'd hired you until you arrived. But I'll be paying 40 per cent of your fee!"

Dr. Bush wasn't really a dictator. He was just a natural-born loner. If you see in yourself any resemblance to Dr. Bush, I'd advise you to stay solo. You'll be happier—and you'll save some other men a lot of grief.

A partnership must meet a demonstrable medical need. I've never known of a truly successful medical partnership that was not founded on a desire to do a better job of doctoring within the framework of a community's medical needs. If this basic urge isn't present, it can't be counterfeited. Sometimes, for example, a physician seeks a partner solely to get relief from physical tiredness. I remember the experience of a G.P. I'll call Dr. Vernon.

"My practice is running me ragged," he told me. "How much can I afford to offer a partner?"

I studied his books and said: "Five thousand a year."

He gasped. "I can't ask a physician to work for that amount."

"I know," I said, "but you asked me how much you could afford. This practice doesn't have enough income, present or prospective, for two men. I'd hire another nurse."

Dr. Vernon disagreed. So he found a partner and gave him 40 per cent of the partnership's net for the first year. After 12 months, the one nurse they had was really busy. But the two doctors weren't. What was too much work for one man left two men with time on their hands. Dr. Vernon was relieved when the partner allowed that he'd like to seek greener pastures.

Now Dr. Vernon and his two nurses are all busy. And they're taking care of the medical needs of their small community very nicely. Dr. Vernon needed help, all right—but not the help of another doctor.

Sometimes a physician seeks a partner for purely competitive reasons. Take Dr. Mason (that's not his real name). He was a busy pediatrician in a New York suburb. When young Dr. Garner, also a pediatrician, told him he planned to hang out his shingle locally on completion of his residency, Dr. Mason figured his practice was threatened. So when Garner showed up, Mason had a partner already installed.

That was five years ago. Now Mason's half of the partnership income is well below his previous solo earnings. What's worse, it's well under Garner's net. Garner won the community's sympathy when Mason tried to freeze him out.

The most misguided motivation for a partnership is personal friendship. Internists Harry Martin and Jack Farrell provide a good example. They came from the same home town. They went through school together. They interned together. They got residencies in the same big hospital. They even married in a double wedding. Then they tried to build a two-man practice, starting from scratch.

After three years, all they had was debts. Their wives finally brought them to their senses. Jack and his wife stayed in the town the friends had chosen for their partnership. Harry and his wife moved away. Both internists are prospering now. Their mistake had been to assume that the town they'd picked to practice in needed both of them.

The lesson to be learned from those three cases is clear. Partnerships not aimed at meeting a community's medical needs are headed for trouble.

Any number can play, but twos and threes in the same field of practice are best. There's no legal limitation, of course, on the number of physicians who can combine. The Mayo Clinic lists 320 doctors' names. And in the most recent directory of medical groups put out by the U.S. Public Health Service you'll find several groups with more than 100 members.

But the big groups, as you'd expect, are always multispecialty outfits—medical supermarkets, you might say. Very few communities can maintain such jumbo-size medical organizations. And the typical American physician isn't anxious to submerge himself in one of them, anyway.

In many small towns it makes economic sense for several doctors in different fields of practice to share space, equipment and personnel. Yet that doesn't necessarily mean they should be partners. They can join forces to build a professional building. They can agree to share the cost of, say, a receptionist, a laboratory or a billing service. But it's not quite so easy to share the work; full partnership for men in different fields of practice is something else again. Here's what I mean:

When Noah was stocking the ark, he took two of each kind. I'll go further and say that three of a kind is better. Three physicians in the same field of practice can provide round-the-clock service throughout the year. And for nine months out of the 12, each man can be exempt from call every third night and every third weekend. He'll have a good chance of being left in peace each second night and each second weekend, too, when he's merely backing up the man on duty. That's a pretty good deal for any physician, in my opinion.

The big risk in partnership is your partner. Years ago, when doctors would ask what drawbacks I saw in medical partnerships, I'd answer in detail. "Your legal liability is broadened," I'd tell them.

"You'll tie up a lot of capital that can't be untied easily. You'll sacrifice a certain amount of independence. You'll even have to adjust some of your ideas about diagnosis and treatment."

Now I simply say: "There aren't any risks, Doctor, if you pick the right partner." And I mean it.

When two good doctors who are also good human beings get together, partnership is a breeze. But if one partner is a bad apple ethically, a professional dunce, a drunk, a fool about money or even a plain ornery cuss—then a wide variety of unpleasant results can ensue.

Your partner's fee-gouging could run *you* out of your medical society. His negligence could cost *you* your life savings. His alcoholic amiability, if it should lead to his signing up happily for X-ray equipment you didn't need, could cost *you* thousands of dollars. These things have happened—and worse.

I've known a debt-ridden doctor to cash insurance checks that belonged to the partnership kitty. He blew $3,000 worth of them before his partner heckled the insurance companies for not paying up—and found that they all had paid.

In a setup where two partners owned an office building jointly, I've seen one pull out and padlock his suite. He kept it locked for two years, until he got his scalper's price for it.

I once steered a young doctor to an older one who was a part-time industrial physician. Senior stipulated that the company's checks shouldn't be part of the partnership income. Junior agreed. Then Junior landed a similar job. Senior said Junior's paycheck came under their income-sharing clause. Junior angrily said he'd give up the job first. Whereupon Senior threatened suit for "failure to use your best efforts to expand the partnership practice."

Of course, it's not likely that you'll run into such troubles. But it *can* happen.

Now let's move on to the big reason you may want to team up:
The right kind of partnership gives you peace of mind. Sound corny? Sure, but I believe it. There's an aura of security around

the doctors I know who are in successful partnerships. It's due to the comforting knowledge that they're buttressed at many key points. For example:

¶ Partners can consult freely and frankly. In problem cases, two heads are better than one. And partners don't have to defend their opinions to each other the way a man is tempted to do when he's consulting with a stranger. In any case, the give-and-take of clinical argument that takes place in a partnership helps keep any man on his professional toes.

¶ Partners can afford more and better facilities. The combined buying power of two or three men often allows them to go in for space and equipment that the solo man can't afford.

¶ Partners get noncompetitive coverage. A partner who sees his colleague's patient has a built-in incentive to protect the absent doctor's interests. And the absentee doctor feels better for knowing that his partner is at bat for him. Two bonuses: The stand-in's clinical approach to the case is probably similar to his partner's, and all the records on the case are at the stand-in's finger tips.

¶ Partners conserve each other's health. Fear of losing income through sickness can haunt the solo practitioner. He's tormented by visions of his patients trooping off to new doctors—and staying with them. But a partner can allow himself enough rest, take adequate vacations and, if he does fall sick, take the time to recuperate as fully as any of his patients. He knows that his partner will hold the fort.

¶ Partners can count on relatively stable incomes. The typical physician hits a fiscal peak in mid-career. Earlier and later, his earnings can be well below the peak. But a young doctor in a partnership commonly escapes the loner's famine years, and the elderly partner's income is more likely to taper off gradually than to nose-dive. Over the years the income of partners follows a flatter curve than that of the solo practitioner. For most family men, at least, that's an advantage.

¶ Partners' investments in their careers are protected. When

7

a solo doctor locks his office door for the last time, he's likely to find that his equipment is worth only peanuts, his former patients are reluctant to square their accounts, and his successor isn't about to pay him anything for the goodwill that took him a lifetime to build. If that same solo doctor dies in harness, it's his widow who discovers these unpalatable truths. But partners—and partners' widows—are luckier, as a rule. They can cash in their assets at an acceptable price because the men they leave behind to carry on have already agreed to it.

Notice I haven't claimed that partners earn more than solo practitioners do. That's because I'm honest; the biggest earners I know all happen to be loners. But I'll say this: Any 100 partners selected at random will average more take-home pay over their professional careers than 100 solo men in the same field of medicine. That's been my experience, and it's borne out by the findings of MEDICAL ECONOMICS' Continuing Survey.

If you've been weighing the pros and cons of partnership, I've one more discovery to pass on to you: *Patients like partnerships.* It isn't so much that they appreciate the bargain they get in having two doctors for the price of one. It's that they feel secure. If you're not available, they know they'll be seen by another doctor they're already acquainted with.

2.

*Two ways
to try it out*

A beaming internist introduced me to his new partner not long ago. "Andy's just finished his residency," he explained. "He'll join me in the practice Monday. We just want you to figure out a painless way for him to buy into my office building."

It wasn't a difficult assignment—not nearly as difficult as the one he gave me three months later. "Unravel this mess," he said. "We're splitting up." In that short time, the partners had proved hopelessly incompatible.

What made this particular failure unusual was that the two doctors were brothers. But it can happen to anyone. I remember the two surgeons who called me in after they decided to split up. They'd been in partnership for five years, but each one told me privately: "I knew before a month was up that I'd made a mistake. Still, I'd invested quite a bit in the venture, so I thought the best thing to do was to try to live with it."

I also remember the three pediatricians who took in a fourth partner. In two weeks they found they had a narcotics addict on their hands.

All three stories make one point clear: You don't have to spend a lifetime with a man to find out that—as far as you're concerned— he's a lemon. In fact, you usually find it out fast. So I always advise a trial period before doctors sign a partnership contract.

An effective expense-sharing agreement

T HIS AGREEMENT made this twentieth day of November, 19—, by and between HAROLD V. HAWKINS, M.D., party of the first part, and CAMPBELL B. SMITH, M.D., party of the second part, WITNESSETH:

WHEREAS, the parties hereto are doctors and desire to engage in their separate practices in the City of Conway, Indiana, but desire also to share the offices now occupied by first party at 111 Park Avenue and to employ office personnel together and to share the expenses therefor on the basis hereinafter set forth and also to share the use of their respective items of equipment;

NOW, THEREFORE, the parties hereto, in consideration of the mutual benefits to be derived therefrom, do hereby contract and agree as follows:

(1) That the parties hereto shall share the offices of first party at 111 Park Avenue in the City of Conway, Indiana, and shall share in the joint expenses of operating said offices, including the following items: rent, electricity, salaries for office help, repairs, furnishings, drugs, supplies, postage, telephone and other items of a like nature.

(2) That to provide a fund for the payment of said joint expenses, the parties hereto shall establish a joint bank account, and each shall deposit the initial sum of Two Thousand Dollars ($2,000.00) therein.

(3) That at the end of each month, the said joint expenses paid

In 77 instances, physicians have taken my advice and have tested their compatibility before pooling assets, liabilities, income and expenses. In seven of these instances, no partnership resulted. Of the partnerships that were set up after the other 70 tryouts, 66 are still in existence.

I've also helped organize 30 partnerships in which the doctors turned thumbs down on my plea for a trial. Ten of those partner-

---

from said account shall be totaled, and each party hereto shall deposit in said account a sum computed by prorating the gross business done by each party in said month against the said joint expenses.

(4) That each party shall continue to own the equipment which he now owns and shall continue to own his separate accounts receivable.

(5) That each party shall separately collect monies due him and may deposit said funds in his own bank account, but that each shall keep careful account of all professional charges and cash receipts and shall make such figures available to the other party as needed for the computation of the said joint expense-sharing.

(6) That each party shall have equal authority as to personnel, but neither shall obligate the association for any sum in excess of One Hundred Dollars ($100.00) without the consent of the other party.

This agreement shall become effective on the second day of January, 19—, and shall continue until terminated. Either party may discontinue this agreement by giving the other a notice in writing of such intention on or before the ninetieth (90th) day prior thereto.

IN WITNESS WHEREOF, the parties hereto have hereunto set their hands and seals to this instrument, executed in duplicate the day and year first above mentioned.
Witnesses:

_____   _____
                                                        First party

_____   _____
                                                        Second party

ships folded—eight of them within less than two years after they were set up.

The figures bear out my contention that you'd best look before you leap: Your chances of succeeding in partnership are 6 to 1 when you try it out first but only 2 to 1 if you plunge right in.

You can pretest a partnership in various ways, but I find two methods—expense-sharing and hiring—the most reliable.

To use the expense-sharing method, you and your prospective partner set up shop in the same office—yours, his or a new one. You practice there for a year or so, holding tight to your respective assets and keeping your earnings separate but sharing running costs. Those costs include rent, phone bills, repairs, salaries of aides used by both doctors and cost of—or depreciation on—furnishings and equipment used jointly. You may split the costs down the middle or prorate them to monthly billings or collections.

If you find yourselves compatible, you form a partnership, pooling your assets and throwing your combined income into the kitty for division according to agreed proportions.

The hiring method is quite different. You hire—or are hired by —another doctor on a fixed salary for a fixed time. It's understood that if the tryout is satisfactory, a partnership will result.

Here, briefly, are the details of each method, with some hints that may help you decide which is best for you:

The expense-sharing method. You and your prospective partner run separate practices in the same office. But you share secretarial and nursing help. You buy supplies jointly. You cover each other for days off, night calls and emergencies. You take care of each other's patients at vacation times. You consult or don't consult on problem cases, as you prefer.

The operating costs of the two practices are paid out of a common fund. You each kick in for the replenishment of this fund every month—equally or unequally, as you think fair. The sample expense-sharing agreement on pages 10-11 will give you an idea of how the plan works. Note that it stipulates that the two practices are separate. There's no foreshadowing of a partnership, nothing about coverage or consultation and no fringe benefits. This arrangement can go on indefinitely or be ended on short notice.

For two doctors who've already built up independent practices in the same community, the expense-sharing method of testing compatibility usually works just fine. Even if they vote against going into full partnership, they can go along under the agreement forever. Or—failing any mutually acceptable settlement—they can end the agreement, tossing a coin to decide who keeps the office and the help.

But if you've already carved out a niche in your community and you plan to bring in a stranger, be wary. You might find later that you've set up a rival. There's something better than expense-sharing in such cases:

The hiring method. Employing a physician may seem even further from the partnership concept than expense-sharing. Not so. The hiring method puts the incentive in the right place: Both men are out to improve the same practice. What's more, the method requires the parties to start out by binding themselves to form a partnership if the tryout succeeds.

The hiring method is simply an updated version of the traditional assistantship, popular in the medical profession for centuries. It's ideal in three common situations: (1) when your prospective partner is much younger than you are, (2) when he's long on training but short on cash and (3) when he's new in town.

If he's young, your direction of and responsibility for his work are big safety factors. You can, for instance, stop him from using procedures you don't approve of. If he's financially strapped, the hiring method will get him started without the drag of debt to make his life miserable. If he's an out-of-towner, you can stipulate that if he turns down your offer of partnership, *and he stays in the area*, he pays you for the start you've given him.

I'm serious about that last point. Look at the prepartnership employment contract on pages 14-15. Notice that Clause 9 does

An effective prepartnership employment contract

THIS AGREEMENT made this sixteenth day of December, 19—, by and between DAVID R. BLEDSOE, M.D., first party, and LEONARD NOVINGER, M.D., second party, WITNESSETH:

WHEREAS, first party is and has been for several years engaged in the practice of medicine and surgery in the City of Melrose, Michigan, and desires to employ second party to assist him in said practice, and second party desires to accept said employment;

NOW, THEREFORE, in consideration of the premises and mutual benefits to be derived herefrom, the parties hereto do hereby contract and agree as follows:

(1) First party does hereby employ second party to assist him in his said practice of medicine and surgery for a period of one (1) year beginning the second day of January, 19—.

(2) Second party agrees to devote his full time and best efforts to the said practice of medicine and surgery, under the direction of first party.

(3) Second party agrees that all fees which may be charged or collected for his services shall be the property of first party.

(4) First party agrees to pay to second party as compensation for his services the sum of One Thousand Dollars ($1,000.00) per month, payable one-half on the first and one-half on the sixteenth day of each month, less any sums which first party is required to withhold by law.

(5) Second party agrees that he will furnish and maintain his own automobile for his own use as may be necessary or desirable in the said practice. Second party also agrees to maintain memberships in the Melrose County Medical Society and such hospital staff organizations or professional societies as may be necessary or desirable.

(6) First party agrees that during the period of this Agreement second party shall be entitled to be absent on vacation without loss of compensation for a period of fourteen days, not necessarily consecutive, such permissible paid absence to include all time spent at professional meetings, post-graduate instructional courses and other meetings of a like kind.

(7) First party agrees that in the event of second party's being unable to perform his duties owing to sickness during the period of this Agreement, his compensation shall not be reduced or withheld until such absence totals more than fourteen days. Second party agrees that if he is absent sick for more than fourteen days during the period of this Agreement, he shall not be entitled to any compensation in respect of such additional days.

(8) It is hereby agreed between the parties that in the final month of this Agreement they will consider together the formation of a partnership, with the intent of forming the same if both parties are satisfied. If a partnership is formed, it is understood that second party will be allotted 30 per cent of the net income in the first year, 35 per cent in the second year, 40 per cent in the third year, 45 per cent in the fourth year and 50 per cent in the fifth year.

(9) Second party for himself agrees and covenants that in the event he is offered a partnership under Clause 8 above and he declines it and enters competitive practice, he will, within thirty days of entering competitive practice, pay to first party the sum of Six Thousand Dollars ($6,000.00) as liquidated damages under this Agreement. For the purpose of this Agreement, the term "competitive practice" shall mean the practice of medicine and surgery, alone or with a partner, as principal or employe, within the County of Melrose during the twenty-four months following the day on which the termination of this employment occurs.

IN WITNESS WHEREOF, the parties hereto have hereunto set their respective hands and seals to this instrument, executed in duplicate the day and year first above mentioned.

Witnesses:

_____ _____
                                                First party

_____ _____
                                                Second party

EDITOR'S NOTE: *This contract and the agreement on pages 10-11 are composite samples. Because they fit no real-life cases exactly, they should not be adapted for actual use without legal advice.*

not bar him from practicing in your town when the employment ends. It says that, if he refuses the partnership you offer him, he must either pay you for introducing him to your community or move along. If he tries to duck the payment, he'll get short shrift from any judge who hears your suit for recovery.

How high should you price that introduction to your community? A lot depends on your estimate of how much harm your prospective partner can do to your practice if he sets up for himself. Don't set the figure so high that a judge can say, "You're being unreasonable, Doctor." My own rule of thumb for the amount to be paid when a hired doctor declines your offer of partnership and enters competitive practice: half the pay he drew from you during the employment period.

If you *don't* offer him a partnership when his employment contract is up, let him hang out his shingle in town without paying you a cent. That's *his* compensation for the disappointing result of the tryout. His presence shouldn't give you any sleepless nights. After all, you let him go because he wasn't good enough to keep.

You can see I'm keen on this pay-if-you-stay clause. In my opinion, it's a big improvement over the clause that requires an ex-associate to leave the area. If you're the associate, it protects you against the man who hires a new boy every year without any intention of ever sharing his lucrative practice. If you're the employer, it protects you against the smart aleck who figures that you won't follow through with a lawsuit if he sticks around and takes care of the patients he cultivated on your time.

Once you've decided to hire a partnership prospect, how much pay should you offer him? Well, it's hard nowadays for a G.P. to round up anyone who'll take less than $10,000 a year; a flat $1,000 a month is common. A young specialist expects and usually gets $12,000 or $15,000 a year. Lately, I've negotiated several employment contracts pegged at $18,000. Figure out what you can afford by estimating the probable net income from your joint work and the minimum amount you can get by on. The difference between the two is the most you can offer. But be sure to offer as much as you can afford.

When you've agreed on the salary, stick with it and resist that impulse to give your associate a bonus if the practice booms during the contract period. I say this for two reasons: (1) If the practice falls on its face, you can't cut his pay. (2) If the practice booms, you can always hike his share of the income when he becomes your partner. Besides, your associate won't have long to wait. Unless the case has some exceptional features, I'd say that the prepartnership period should run about one year. As I've indicated, it won't take long to find out that Junior—or Senior—won't do.

But of course you both hope that he *will* do. So be prepared: Discuss the terms of the partnership *at the time of the initial hiring* and come to tentative agreement on the basic clauses. If you're the man in possession, tell your new associate how long it will be before he can expect to be your 50-50 partner. Tell him how much annual vacation you think would be right for each of you. Let him know what you think should happen if either of you falls sick, is permanently disabled, gets too old to practice or dies.

Tell him, too, what strikes you as a fair price for a full partnership interest in your office building, your equipment and your accounts receivable. Sketch out a plan, if you can, that will let him pay his way and still have enough to let him live respectably while he's on the short end of the partnership profits. The more you tell him and the more questions you answer, the likelier he is to stay, once he accepts your proposition.

The one question you should not answer too soon is the Big One: "How am I doing?" He'll ask it before a month is up. Fight down the urge to say, "Just fine!" If you do say something like that, you might get into the same fix as an OBG man I know. After three months of pestering, he told his associate: "You're doing great." The associate said: "Well, why wait till the year's up? Let's sign the partnership contract now." They signed. One month later, the new partner was arrested for doing abortions.

3.

Getting a partnership started

When a young Massachusetts internist became the partner of an older colleague a few months ago, I priced the firm's physical assets—cash, furnishings, equipment and supplies but *not* accounts receivable—at $14,450. The young man's contribution to that total was just $50—the value of a pigskin medical bag. Everything else in the office, even the change in the cashbox, belonged to his partner.

This lopsided situation raised a question that all new partnerships must answer: *Who puts up how much?*

In tangible assets, the young internist had nothing more than his bag to put up. As an equalizer, he agreed to pay his partner $200 a month out of his share of the partnership's earnings for the first three years. When he finally signs check number 36, he'll have contributed $7,200, and he'll then own half of the firm's tangible assets. At the same time, he'll start collecting 50 per cent of the partnership's net income, instead of the 35 per cent he gets now.

The month after the Massachusetts internists made that agreement, two Tennessee G.P.s joined forces. They planned to allow 60 per cent of the partnership's net income to one partner, 40 per cent to the other, until further notice. But how to arrange their ownership of the assets?

Their answer was to figure out the book value* of the equipment, furniture and furnishings each was bringing to the new office. The 60-per-cent man was contributing $4,800 more than his partner. So the partners agreed that the 40-per-cent man should pay his partner $1,920 in cash—40 per cent of the difference between their contributions. Their ownership immediately became proportionate to their shares of net income.

About the same time, two Arizona pediatricians were showing visitors round their big new clinic. The building had a $60,000 mortgage on it. Its $15,000 worth of new equipment had been bought with borrowed cash. Each partner had already put up half the cost of the land the clinic stood on. Each had paid half the down payment on the building. And each agreed to be equally liable for the mortgage and equipment loans. Thus, their ownership stood at 50-50 from the start. And this ratio was the right one, since they'd agreed to split the clinic's earnings right down the middle.

I've cited these three cases to illustrate a good general rule: Who puts up how much depends on who gets how much. I feel that ownership of assets in a partnership should be directly related to the distribution of profits.

Some other people apparently don't feel that way. I've met scores of doctors who've matched their partners dollar for dollar in assets just to simplify their bookkeeping. They don't seem to realize that, if their income isn't also divided equally, it isn't a fair deal. The man who puts up half the capital in return for less than half the earnings is contributing more than his share.

---

*Original cost less depreciation claimed to date on Federal income tax returns.

Who puts up how much is only one of several posers you'll encounter when you plan a partnership. Below are some others you should think and talk about before calling in an attorney to write a partnership agreement:

How much starting cash do you need? If you and your partner have worked together under a prepartnership agreement for a year or so, there's probably enough money in the till to start things off. In the case of the Massachusetts internists I mentioned, the older man had employed the younger for a year. There was enough cash in his professional bank balance to get the partnership going. If they'd been sharing expenses for a year, each partner (instead of just one) would have had a bank balance he could sign over to the partnership account.

But if you're pooling two existing practices, as did the Tennessee G.P.s I mentioned, you may need to raise some extra cash. Moving into new premises, as they did, you may find that some of your possessions aren't suited to the new office. So money may have to be spent for replacements.

Aside from what's needed for new equipment, though, it doesn't take much cash to meld two existing practices. More cash is needed when a brand-new practice begins. This was true with the Arizona pediatricians. Besides their cash payments for land and building, they needed quite a hunk of money to meet their various loan installments, deposits on utilities and phones, first month's payroll and the cost of consumable supplies—everything from stationery to tongue depressors. They had to raise $2,000 apiece in cash to meet these expenses at the start.

How do you handle the office building owned by one partner? In my observation, it's not a good idea for a medical partnership to own real estate. Such ownership can lead to too many complications. I'd recommend that, if you own the office, you rent it to the partnership rather than make it a partnership asset. In case you want your partner to share the ownership of the building where you'll practice—and if he's of the same mind—sell him a half-interest or less. As co-owners of the property, the two of you can then rent it to the partnership.

Another solution: Set up a corporation to own the building and to lease it to the partnership. Then sell shares of stock in the corporation to your partner. When your partnership ends, as some day it must, it's simpler to transfer a handful of share certificates than a title to half a building.

What do you do about accounts receivable? Let's go back to the partnerships I've already mentioned. The young Massachusetts internist, never having had patients of his own, had no accounts receivable. His partner's patients owed $30,000. You might think it would be simplest to keep those debts out of the partnership and let the senior partner collect them on his own. But that solution wouldn't be as simple as it looked.

Their bookkeeper would have to set up two income accounts: one for old receivables belonging to the senior partner and the other for new receivables belonging to both partners. Besides causing bookkeeping confusion, this arrangement would give Junior nothing to live on for a while. His 35 per cent of the first month's net income, for example, would be 35 per cent of a deficit. One office rent day and four weekly office paydays would arrive before the partnership would be ready to mail out its first statements to patients.

So they settled it in a way that will suit many other new senior-junior partnerships:

¶ All accounts considered uncollectible ($3,000) were deducted from the total owed Senior ($30,000), leaving a balance due him of $27,000.

¶ All collections on old *and* new accounts were channeled into the partnership kitty.

¶ Senior was given the right for three years to draw $9,000 annually "off the top"—that is, before partnership earnings are divided—to compensate him for his collectibles.

After the first three years, when Junior starts collecting a full

50 per cent of the partnership's earnings, he'll own half of the accounts receivable as they then stand. Senior will have been paid off.

Another solution to the accounts receivable problem was worked out by the two Tennessee G.P.s I described earlier. The 60-per-cent partner had $16,000 in collectible accounts. The 40-per-cent partner had $12,000. If the total $28,000 went into the partnership kitty, one man stood to get $16,800, the other $11,200. This was so close to the right ratio that they handled their own receivables just as they'd handle new ones. Said the 40-per-cent partner cheerfully: "It's worth $800 to me to keep things simple."

As for the Arizona pediatricians, they had no receivables problem—because they had no receivables. One partner explained: "We're both escapees from the same salaried group. We've collected all we're ever going to get from that quarter."

What expenses does the partnership pay? It will, of course, pick up the tab for office rent, utilities, salaries, supplies, phone bills, business taxes, various kinds of insurance and such. But should it pay, for instance, the partners' auto expenses?

I generally recommend against it. I've run across too many situations like these:

¶ In a three-man OBG partnership in California, one doctor drove a Lincoln Continental, one a Chevrolet sedan and one a Volkswagen. On equal mileage, the largest car gulped more gas in 10 days than the smallest did in a month. The VW owner felt aggrieved because, through the partnership, he was paying part of the other cars' costs.

¶ Two G.P. partners who lived and practiced in a New York exurb decided to draw $50 a month each for auto expenses and to pay such bills themselves. Then one of them moved 10 miles farther away from the office. He's convinced that he's being gypped because his auto expenses are now more than $50 a month. But his partner doesn't see it that way.

¶ In Florida, two internists agreed they'd each lease a Thunderbird and charge the rentals to the partnership account. One man, a bachelor, didn't need a second car. The other, married with five kids, did. Finally the family man suggested that the bachelor pay back half his T-Bird rental for "personal use." They argued about it briefly, then gave up their leases.

You'll avoid such arguments if you pay your own auto expenses. Don't worry about the tax angle, because there isn't one. The deduction is worth just as much on your personal income tax return as it is on the partnership's.

As a rule, I also recommend keeping professional travel expenses out of the partnership books. Sure, trips to medical conventions and seminars are legitimate expenses. Tax-deductible, too. But if you charge them to the firm, here's what can happen:

¶ In one year, a member of a six-man Pennsylvania partnership attended medical meetings in San Francisco, New Orleans, Miami Beach and Sea Island, Ga. Time absent, 18 days, all of which were charged to him as vacation time. But his trips cost the partnership $1,100. I asked why the group didn't stop the traveling member. "Stop him? Heck, I don't want to stop him," the oldest member said irritably. "I just want him to use his own money."

¶ Two Midwest surgeons always go to conventions together. They get a solo man to cover while they're gone—and sometimes lose cases to him. I asked why they didn't divide their trips. "We used to," one said. "I'd pay half of my partner's expenses to New York. He'd pay half of mine to a meeting 20 miles away. The way we do it now is expensive, but it keeps the peace."

If you exclude professional travel from your list of approved partnership expenses, the peace won't be fractured on account of it.

Professional entertainment is another king-sized headache if paid through the partnership. Here's the sort of thing I mean:

¶ In a senior-junior partnership of Georgia ophthalmologists, Senior and his wife are gregarious. She throws four or five big parties a year and invites plenty of doctors and their wives. Her husband takes G.P.s duck-hunting. Last year, he charged the partnership $1,200 for such activities. And Junior is upset about the 40 per cent of it that comes out of his pocket.

¶ A three-man team in Louisiana owns a boat and a riverside cabin. The first year, all three partners took professional guests on outings. Then the novelty wore off. Now the boat and cabin are used by only one partner—the one who proposed their purchase in the first place. The other two partners feel they're paying for fun they don't have, but they can't get up enough nerve to propose a sale.

If you're tempted to charge all professional entertainment costs off to the partnership on the theory that this improves their deductibility—well, I must admit this is true in certain cases. Some T-men are more tolerant of tax deductions that several partners have agreed on; they're less tolerant of an individual's claims. In my opinion, though, it's still better to handle entertainment expenses outside the partnership. It's fairer to the partners, and that's what counts most.

4.
Equal work,
equal pay

I am a strong advocate of financial equality for partners practicing together in the same field—and for equality not too long delayed. Almost all the small, single-specialty partnerships I've helped get started have accepted the logic of this point of view. They have therefore agreed to divide earnings equally, either at once or within five years.

To see why, sit in with me at a conference with two doctors who are about to sign a formal partnership agreement. The two doctors have worked together for a full year. During that year, the younger man was on salary. Now satisfied that they make a good team, they're ready to form a partnership.

The conference to do so is being held in the home of Dr. Michael Wainhouse, the senior man. His partner-to-be is Dr. Colin Bell, and of course I'm present, too. On the table before us lies the partnership agreement. One of its clauses says that the two partners' earnings shall be shared on a 70-30 basis the first year, 65-35 the second year and so on until a 50-50 division is reached for the fifth and all subsequent years. (See the sample clause in the box on this page.) Now listen. . . .

DR. WAINHOUSE: Tell me, do all partners end up by splitting earnings equally?

COTTON: Not all. But if they're in the same field of practice, as you two are, most of them do. Generally, one of the main objectives in such partnerships is equal work. That naturally leads to equal pay.

DR. BELL: Isn't five years rather a long time to wait for equal

---

Income clause for a two-man partnership

A void vague phraseology in this important clause. Don't refer to "first party" and "second party" or "first year" or "second year." State each man's name and the percentage he's to get, with the exact dates on which any changes are to occur.

An example—not to be adapted for actual use without legal advice— is the income clause below. Elsewhere, the contract specifies that net income is what remains after partnership expenses have been paid out of the common kitty.

The monthly net income as defined in this agreement shall be shared by the partners on a percentage basis as follows, as of April 1 each year:

	1964	1965	1966	1967	1968 on
Michael Wainhouse, M.D.	70%	65%	60%	55%	50%
Colin Bell, M.D.	30%	35%	40%	45%	50%

The distribution of the said monthly net income shall be made not later than the tenth of the month following the month in which it is earned.

---

pay? Remember, I've already worked here a year. And I'm already 30 years old—and broke.

Cotton: I'm sorry, Doctor, but that year you spent on salary doesn't enter into this new situation. As a partner, you start April 1, assuming this agreement goes into effect. Four years from now, when you'll be starting your fifth year as a partner, you'll begin to get 50 cents of every dollar the partnership nets.

Dr. Wainhouse: And there'll probably be more net dollars than there are now. You'll be doing pretty well at the age of 34, Colin. Seems to me I've heard of men waiting much longer.

Cotton: You have. Some highly respected management consultants advise much longer waits. They argue that the founder of a practice should continue to get most of its income for as long as 10 or 15 years. How'd you like to inch up two percentage points a year, Dr. Bell? That would postpone your equal share until you were 40.

Dr. Bell: Frankly, I wouldn't sign an agreement like that. But why don't *you* advise that kind of deal?

Cotton: Simple. I noticed years ago that an established physician rarely loses money by taking on a partner. Sure, his income may drop a little in the prepartnership year. That's when he pays a fixed salary to a man who at first merely helps him take care of the patients he already has. But after that year on salary, the new man nearly always has his own following of new patients. So in the first partnership year, the founder has a good chance of taking home more cash than he did in his last solo year. And Dr. Wainhouse agrees with me that the senior man should reward the junior promptly for such practice-building.

Dr. Bell: I don't want Mike to think I'm ungrateful, but I've been earning half our office income for these past three months. At least I've seen as many patients as Mike has, if not more. We've shared night work and weekend work equally. So I can't help wondering how you arrive at that low starting share of 30 per cent for me.

COTTON: A fair question, and the answer's in two parts. First, not all the patients you've seen during the last three months were new to this practice—not by a long shot. I have some figures here showing that over the past year the practice netted just 25 per cent more than it did the last year Dr. Wainhouse was alone. Some of that extra money was paid out to you as salary. Suppose we credit *all* that growth to you.

DR. BELL: That gives me 25 per cent to start with?

COTTON: Bad arithmetic, Dr. Bell. The practice netted 125 per cent of its previous net. You get credit for 25 of that 125; in other words, you get credit for one-fifth of the new net. So we start you off with 20 per cent and add something for your help with the old patients.

DR. BELL: So you're adding 10 per cent of the old net?

COTTON: Figure it again. We're adding 10 per cent of 125— the *new* net—so we're really giving you 12½ per cent of the old net. In short, you start off with all the money from this past year's new patients plus one-eighth of the money from Dr. Wainhouse's old patients.

DR. WAINHOUSE: And that leaves me with seven-eighths of the money from my old patients. Of course, next year I'll also get 70 per cent of the money from patients we add during the year. My percentage of new money will drop every year, but I'm betting that there'll be enough new money each year to keep my income at its present level.

COTTON: Dr. Bell, that's the second part of my answer to your question about how we determined your starting figure. We wanted to protect Dr. Wainhouse against a sharp drop in his take-home pay. Before you came, he was pretty well off but too busy. While you're giving him the help he needs, there's a limit to the amount of cash he can afford to give up in exchange for that help. With the percentages we've worked out, he won't suffer much of a drop. And I hope—and expect—that there will be enough new patients each year so that his income won't drop at all.

DR. WAINHOUSE: What if it doesn't work out that way? Does Colin still get his 50 per cent four years from now?

COTTON: Yes, he does. Suppose the practice's growth comes to a halt at, say, 140 per cent of what you netted the last year you practiced alone. You'll end up with only 70 per cent of that year's earnings, and Dr. Bell will get much less than he now hopes for. So both of you will be disappointed. But what usually happens when any sort of a business venture doesn't pan out?

DR. WAINHOUSE: I get it. We liquidate.

COTTON: Or reorganize. After all, you can negotiate a new deal at any time. . . .

Our conversation from then on went into the income-sharing variations and refinements that I'll describe in my next chapter. But you should know the upshot: Drs. Wainhouse and Bell agreed on the income-sharing principles described here. In my experience, most two-man partnerships do.

Withdrawal accounts for two partners

The income clause reproduced on page 28 specifies that shares shall be paid out by the tenth of each month. Many partners prefer to be paid more often. For such men, I suggest this:

On the first of each month: Pay a previously agreed amount—say, $1,000—to each partner. This should enable him to take care of the house mortgage and any other big bills due early in the month.

On the tenth of each month: The books for the previous month having by this time been closed out, pay each partner the remaining portion of his share.

If a partner needs extra cash: Advance him money up to a maximum previously agreed upon. Charge it to his withdrawal account and subtract it from the next payment due him.

5.

Dividing the income in two

The division of partnership income can be tailored to fit any circumstances. In the usual situation, as I described it in the previous chapter, an older man going into partnership with a younger man starts him off with 30 per cent of the practice net. He increases this share by five percentage points a year until they're dividing the net 50-50. That's the usual way. But it's not universal.

I've seen partners start off at 50-50, at 80-20, and at almost every ratio in between. I've even seen some partnership agreements where the founder of the practice took the smaller percentage.

For example, a 66-year-old radiologist, hit by a mild coronary thrombosis, gave his hurriedly acquired partner 60 per cent of the net immediately. The quid pro quo was that the senior man was to work only six hours a day, five days a week, and was to be exempt from emergency work.

By contrast, I know an elderly G.P. who got a new-fledged

M.D. to come in with him at only one-third of the net for five years. The carrot at the end of the stick: Senior bound himself to retire completely at the end of that time and to turn the entire practice over to Junior.

You may have heard of deals in which part of Junior's share isn't turned over to him at the time he earns it. It's held in escrow for some time, the theory being that this will discourage him from pulling out. I've never assisted with such an arrangement, nor do I ever want to. I fail to see the validity of withholding fairly earned cash from a young man who undoubtedly needs it and who is being taxed on it.

A good income-sharing plan is one that makes each partner confident he's getting a fair shake. It needn't follow the standard pattern. For instance, I've run across these custom-tailored twists:

A guaranteed minimum to the founder. A young internist in Texas consented to take whatever was left each year after his senior partner had drawn $30,000. The first year, Junior got $13,000. After four years, he began to get more than Senior. That's when they reworked their partnership agreement to provide for a 50-50 split.

A guaranteed minimum to the newcomer. A Pennsylvania orthopedist offered a new partner 25 per cent of the net or $18,000, whichever was greater, for each of the first two years of their partnership. The first year, 25 per cent of the net came to only $14,000, so Junior got his minimum of $18,000. But the next year the partnership netted $96,000, so Junior collected $24,000. The partners then decided that no guaranteed minimum was necessary in the future. They settled on a 60-40 split, with Senior receiving the higher percentage, and changed to 50-50 after two more years.

Guarantees to both partners. Two general practitioners in New Jersey agreed to start thus: The first $40,000 of annual net income would be split 75-25—that is, $30,000 to the founder and $10,000 to the new man. Any excess would be shared equally. Each year, Senior's guarantee was to drop by $5,000, and Junior's was to rise by that amount, until the guarantees were equal. Then they'd be dispensed with: The partners would continue on a straight 50-50 basis. What if the net fell below $40,000 in any guarantee year? According to their agreement, Junior was to get his $10,000 first. But they never had such a year.

Shares based partly on production. Two Georgia pediatricians shared their partnership income equally for two years. Then one man became unhappy about his return because he had consistently put more business on the books than his partner had. Their solution: Divide one-half of the joint net on a 50-50 basis and split the remaining half according to each partner's record of business done. Last year, they grossed $70,000, and one partner was responsible for $40,000 of that sum. After expenses were paid, they had $50,000 to divide. One partner received $26,786 (half of $25,000 plus four-sevenths of $25,000); the other partner received $23,214 (half of $25,000 plus three-sevenths of $25,000).

Every man for himself. Occasionally I come across partners whose shares are based entirely on production. If one partner brings in, say, two-thirds of the total business, he pays two-thirds of the expenses and keeps two-thirds of what's left over. In my book, such a partnership is more correctly called cooperative practice. Or even competitive practice with a few fringe benefits. It still seems to me that if two partners share the work on an equal basis, they should eventually share income in the same way.

6.
Fair shares
for three or more

Most two-man partnerships I know divide their net earnings on a percentage basis. But when there are one or more additional partners, I've found it advantageous to junk percentages in favor of a simple point system.

That word "simple" is important. The more familiar point systems allow for prestige, training, seniority, diligence, billings and other factors that admittedly enter into the economics of medical partnerships. Typically, such systems provide a base salary with trimmings—that is, they allow extra pay for factors like those I've listed above.

I'm not knocking those systems. They have their uses for large groups. But three- or four- or five-man partnerships don't need such complicated formulas. The following example shows the benefits of a simpler point plan:

When Dr. Francis took on Dr. Kearney as a partner, he gave

the younger man 30 per cent of their combined net and agreed to raise his share by five percentage points every year until they were sharing on a 50-50 basis. But by the time Kearney was getting 40 per cent, the booming practice needed a third man. They picked Dr. Joseph.

Francis and Kearney wanted to preserve their original agreement to arrive at equality with each other in two more years. They also wanted to put Joseph on a rising percentage basis two

---

Income clause for a three-man partnership

An example—not to be adapted for actual use without legal advice—is the income clause below. Elsewhere it's specified that net income is what remains after partnership expenses have been paid out of the common kitty.

The monthly net income as defined in this agreement shall be shared among the partners proportionately to the points allotted each of them as follows, as of April 1 each year:

	1964	1965	1966	1967	1968 on
Theodore Francis, M.D.	20	20	20	20	20
Ralph Kearney, M.D.	12	16	20	20	20
Albert Joseph, M.D.	8	11	14	17	20
Total points	40	47	54	57	60

The distribution shall be made in the following manner: The net income for each month shall be divided by the total points of all the partners to determine the value of one point, and the share of each partner for that month shall be the value of one point multiplied by the number of points to which he is entitled. Distribution of monthly net income shall be made not later than the tenth day of the month following the month in which it is earned.

---

years behind Kearney. Rather than run into a lot of intricate paper work scaling down two percentages to make room for a third, they did this:

¶ Francis's share was pegged at 20 points. And he'll have 20 points while the partnership lasts.

¶ Kearney got 12 points. And he'll get a 4-point raise in each of the next two years.

¶ Joseph started out with 8 points. And he'll get a 3-point raise in each of the next four years.

Translating points into dollar shares is a cinch. After the partnership's net income is known, it's divided by the total number of points then credited to the three partners—40 the first year. There's the dollar value per point. Multiply it by each partner's points, and you have his dollar share.

When Joseph gets his last pay hike, each man will have 20 points, so the net will then be split three equal ways. And if a fourth man is taken into the partnership, as may well happen, they'll just fix his starting points and his rate of progression without in any way disturbing the relative status of Francis, Kearney and Joseph.

This simple point system pointing toward equality works well with single-specialty or all-G.P. partnerships. But when doctors in different specialties pool their earnings, the goal of equality is often unrealistic.

Take a case I ran across recently. Three G.P.s, a general surgeon and a pediatrician chipped in equal amounts to build a much-needed medical building in a small Ohio community. Then they decided to go further and combine their practices in a partnership. They also decided that an equal division of income would be fair —one-fifth to each partner.

What the Ohio doctors didn't realize was that some fields of practice consistently produce less income than others, even though the men in those fields work as long and as hard as their colleagues in other fields. At the end of the first year when they took stock of the situation, the quintet found that they'd produced these percentages of their partnership's gross income:

$$
\begin{aligned}
\text{Surgeon} & \dots\dots\dots\dots\dots & 30\% \\
\text{G.P. No. 1} & \dots\dots\dots\dots & 24 \\
\text{G.P. No. 2} & \dots\dots\dots\dots & 18 \\
\text{G.P. No. 3} & \dots\dots\dots\dots & 16 \\
\text{Pediatrician} & \dots\dots\dots\dots & 12
\end{aligned}
$$

The pediatrician was the first one to see the significance of this. "My one-fifth share," he said, "is way out of line. Getting this much makes me uncomfortable." He moved to call off the whole arrangement.

But the surgeon demurred. "I like working with this team," he said. "There must be a fair way for us to share the money." There was: a modification of the simple point plan that had solved the Francis-Kearney-Joseph problem.

Using each man's contribution to gross income as a rough guide, the five Ohioans parceled out the points this way:

¶ The surgeon got 20 points.

¶ G.P. No. 1 got 18 points.

¶ The other two G.P.s and the pediatrician each got 16 points.

The total points for the five men add up to 86. Each month, therefore, they divide their combined net income by this number and then multiply the result by a man's assigned points. That's his monthly cash share—and, as all five of the partners see it, it's a fair compromise between equality and earning power.

7.
The basic fringe benefits

There's a mistaken notion among many physicians that the fringe benefits enjoyed by employes in industry and commerce are denied to nonsalaried professional men. The fact is, two or more medical partners can set up as tidy a package of fringe benefits as anyone could wish. I know many doctors who have done just that. For example:

¶ A sun-loving New York pediatrician spends happy winters in a pink villa on the French Riviera. His partner keeps the New York practice going while he's away. Come summer, the partner will head for the Canadian north woods and stay there three months while the sun-worshiper carries on the practice.

¶ A G.P. in Michigan was laid up for six months last year with a coronary occlusion. His income for the year, though, was within $100 of what he'd have earned if he'd worked the whole 12 months. His partners came through with enough hard work—and hard cash—to supplement the G.P.'s disability insurance checks by that much.

¶ The career of a prominent Texas orthopedist was wrecked by a Dupuytren's contracture of the right hand. He's now learning a new job as a securities salesman in his brother's office. Meanwhile, for more than a year now, he's received a check every month from his former partners. The checks will keep coming for almost two years more. "By that time," he says cheerfully, "I hope to be well-established on Wall Street."

¶ One of my long-time clients in New Jersey will be 65 this year, and he plans to quit practice. He's due for retirement pay from his present partners until he's 80.

¶ A doctor's widow in Alabama draws a monthly allowance from her husband's former partner. It's her husband's share of the accounts receivable when he died. The monthly allowance will stop when she's drawn it five years—but by then, she'll have col-

---

Sample vacation clause for a partnership agreement

Each partner shall be entitled to a vacation of 30 days in each calendar year (pro rata for the first year if not a full year) without loss of his share of earnings. For any additional vacation absence, the absent partner shall not receive any earnings, and his forfeited share shall pass to the other. Vacation days need not be consecutive. Vacation leave may be accumulated but not beyond a point at which any partner shall be entitled to more than three months' vacation in any one calendar year.

EDITOR'S NOTE: *The clauses shown here and on pages 43-46 are composite samples. Because they fit no real-life cases exactly, they should not be adapted for actual use without legal advice.*

---

lected some $24,000. And that's over and above the substantial check she got for her husband's interest in the partnership's office building and its contents.

To get such fringe benefits for yourself or your wife, all you need is a good partner and a belief in the Golden Rule. Then you can wrap up the package that suits you best. Anticipating that you'll probably have a partner some day if you don't already have one, here are some of the possibilities:

Vacation benefits. How much vacation time can the practice pay for? Try to make it a full month for each partner. Whatever you decide, don't be vague. State clearly in your partnership contract how long each partner may be absent each year without loss of pay. And specify exactly what's to happen to the pay a partner loses if he overstays his leave. (See sample clause on page 42.)

Sick-leave benefits. Who knows better than you do that most human illnesses last a short time and end in full recovery? Know-

---

Sample sick-leave clause for a partnership agreement

Each partner shall be entitled to sickness absence, if necessary, not exceeding four weeks in any 12 months, without loss of his share of earnings. In case of additional sickness absence, the absent partner shall receive (a) for additional absence up to eight weeks, one-half of the share he would have received but for his absence, and (b) for absence beyond the eight weeks mentioned in (a) above, no share of earnings until his return to the practice. If a partner absent sick does not return to the practice within 12 months of the start of his absence and is not entitled to retire on the ground of total and permanent disability, the partnership shall be terminated on the completion of his 12 months' absence. All forfeited earnings of an absent partner under (a) and (b) above shall pass to the other partner.

---

ing this, you and your partner might well decide to be generous with each other when ordinary ailments keep you away from work. Your best bet is to agree to send full paychecks for a reasonable time, then reduce the cash flow to half and, finally, cut it off. What's a reasonable time? One month on full pay followed by two months on half-pay. That's about as much as most small partnerships can stand in a year. (See sample clause on page 43.)

Total-disability benefits. If, like the Texas orthopedist I mentioned earlier, a partner is hit by an ailment that ends his medical career, he needs more than short-term financial aid. Why not give him full pay for, say, three months, plus an extra week for each year of partnership service? (See sample clause below.) Thus, if

---

Sample permanent-disability clause for a partnership agreement

If a partner is unable to practice his profession by reason of total and permanent physical or mental disability and is thereby compelled to retire from this partnership, leaving the practice to be continued by the other (with or without a new partner or partners), the incapacitated partner shall furnish acceptable medical evidence of his disability and shall thereupon be entitled to disability retirement leave with full pay as follows:

From the date of certification of disability, 12 weeks.

Plus for each completed year of partnership under this agreement, one week.

Plus for David Jameson, M.D., in recognition of his prior contributions to this practice, 12 weeks.

If a partner dies while receiving disability pay, the provisions of this agreement respecting the death of a partner shall operate as of the date of death, to the exclusion of this disability clause.

---

your 50-50 partner of 12 years' standing should suffer a disabling stroke, you would share your earnings with him for half a year.

Sound too generous? Remember, it's something you'll never have to do twice for the same partner. And in case it's you who suffers total disability, *he'll* be helping *you* through a bad time.

Retirement benefits. Not many doctors salt away enough cash in their peak years to assure a comfortable retirement. And recent legislation notwithstanding, the solo physician's hopes of a worry-free old age aren't apt to zoom any time soon. But for doctors in partnership, retirement at 65 or 70 can be highly practicable. Here's a real-life example:

Dr. Beal, well into his 60s, told his partner, Dr. Daly: "I've had

---

Sample retirement clause
for a partnership agreement

A partner who, on or after attaining the age of 65 years, wishes to retire from the practice of medicine and from this partnership, leaving the practice to be continued by the other (with or without a new partner), shall (a) give not less than 90 days' notice of his intention to retire; (b) at the expiration of such notice, receive retirement pay on the same basis as if he had retired because of disability; and (c) at the expiration of his retirement leave, transfer his interest in the partnership assets and accounts receivable in the manner provided herein for the transfer of a deceased partner's interest.

If a partner dies while on retirement leave, the provisions of this agreement respecting the death of a partner shall operate as of the date of death, to the exclusion of this retirement clause. If a former partner dies after completing his retirement leave but before the transfer of his interest has been completed, all remaining payments still due shall be made to his estate or named beneficiary.

Sample death clause for a partnership agreement

If a partner dies while this agreement is in force, the survivor shall pay to the estate or to the named beneficiary of the decedent the following amounts:

The capital account of the decedent as of the end of the month preceding the death. It is agreed that accounts receivable from patients for professional services are not capital assets for this purpose.

2. The decedent's share of net income, if any, calculated up to the date of death and not already paid.

3. The decedent's share, according to the proportions ruling at the date of death, of accounts receivable from patients for professional services rendered by the partnership prior to the date of death.

Said share of accounts receivable shall be paid over monthly to the estate or named beneficiary as collected by the survivor for a period of 12 months from the date of death only.

The survivor and the estate or named beneficiary may agree upon a lump-sum payment in lieu of the share of accounts receivable, in which event the lump sum shall be computed as follows: The accounts receivable shall be scrutinized by a competent person or firm, and those deemed to be uncollectible shall be deleted. The estate or named beneficiary shall receive the decedent's share of the total remaining, less 20 per cent for anticipated collection losses and the costs of collection. The survivor and the estate or named beneficiary may agree to pay and receive the amount due in installments payable at such intervals and over such a period of time as they may jointly decide.

---

it, Sam. Me for the quiet life. Send me my share of the receivables when they're paid." Said Dr. Daly: "Hold on, Joe. Your share of the receivables may be worth about $10,000 in cash within a year. But if you take it all at once, on top of your peak earnings this year, you'll have to turn around and pay most of it to Uncle Sam. What say I send you $140 a month for six years instead?"

They made the deal. So the Federal income tax on Dr. Beal's $10,000 is being stretched over six years and paid at rock-bottom rates.

Is it feasible for the partners in a two-man firm to promise each other a lifetime retirement income? I don't think so. But they can say to each other: "Leave your assets and accounts receivable with me, and I'll send you a check every month for a long, long time." How long the checks keep going out depends on what the partners have to work with. If the retiring doctor dies before the promised payments are completed, the remaining checks can go to his heirs.

For men much younger than their partners, the problem sometimes is how to encourage an oldster to quit. Good solution: a clause in your contract offering the senior a period of retirement leave with full pay. The retirement pay—computed, perhaps, on the same basis as disability benefits—serves the same purpose as buying goodwill. But it also has this advantage: You can tax-deduct the retirement pay, while a goodwill purchase is not deductible. (See sample retirement clause on page 45.)

Death benefits. Every day in the United States three or four solo physicians die. What follows is often sad to see. The widow sells off her late husband's office equipment for the best price she can get and then does what she can to collect outstanding bills. Usually she takes a financial beating. But partners' widows can be spared all this.

How? Well, you can agree that, if one partner dies, the other will pay a fair price for the decedent's share of the tangible assets—i.e., any office building and equipment owned by the partnership. Since the survivor will carry on the practice, he'll be better able to collect old bills than any widow will ever be. He can then turn over to her whatever proportion her husband would have received out of them.

If you're the survivor, you can go even further. Instead of giving the widow a lump sum or the large amounts she'll be entitled to in the first couple of months, you can offer her steady monthly payments over a number of years. If you do, she'll be able to keep more of the money after taxes, and you'll get a cash supply that can help you hire your next partner.

A Tennessee surgeon and his partner's widow made such an arrangement last June soon after the partner died. The widow agreed to draw $300 a month for seven years. If she'd taken the money as it flooded in during the last six months of the year, the Internal Revenue Service would have taken almost 50 per cent of it. That's because the receivables—added to her husband's income

---

Should you insure your partner's life?

Doctor-partners often buy life insurance on either themselves or each other with the survivor as beneficiary. The surviving partner turns over the insurance proceeds he gets to the widow in full or part settlement for her husband's interest in the partnership's assets and receivables.

When medical partners of different ages take out insurance for identical amounts, the partner paying the higher premiums makes a bad bargain. Still, it may be prudent in some situations to insure for the cash to buy out a widow's interest in, say, an office building or high-cost equipment.

But don't take out life insurance with the idea of using the proceeds to buy her husband's share of the accounts receivable. If you pay premiums for 20 years, you may pay out as much as you could hope to collect from your partner's accounts. Besides, you can't possibly forecast what your partner's receivables will be worth when he dies. So you're likely to insure for too much or too little.

My advice: Either collect the accounts receivable and pay out the widow's share as the money comes in or buy them from her on the installment plan described above.

---

up to June—would have put her into a high income tax bracket. But as things are, the I.R.S. gets only about 15 per cent of her monthly payments.

In a partnership contract, how do you settle just how much a widow is to get? It's best not to name a dollar figure. Instead, use a formula tied to the accounts receivable as they stand at the time of the death. Allow for the inevitable collection losses. And arrange the monthly payment and the pay-off period with the widow, not with your partner while he's alive. That way, the payments can be set to match her known needs. (See sample clause on page 46.)

Should you limit the widow's payment to what her husband would have drawn had he lived? Not necessarily. You can consider more generous treatment in recognition of the deceased doctor's contributions to the goodwill value of the partnership. That's something for you and your partner to discuss.

Want more fringe benefits? Here's a selection from some of the contracts I've helped hammer out:

¶ One or two weeks' paid absence each year for the purpose of attending conventions, seminars, etc. That time is in addition to the annual month's vacation.

¶ Some income during cold-war military service. (But keep away from any clause that guarantees pay during a hot war.)

¶ Financial assistance when a partner drops out for time to take a specialty residency. (But be sure to arrange for this in your partnership agreement: If the new specialist doesn't come back to the old practice, he pays back all or part of the money.)

8.

More advanced fringe benefits

Two can live as cheaply as one, they say. Well, in planning fringe benefits for more than 100 medical partnerships, I've found that three—or more—can live more cheaply than two. It stands to reason that two men can afford to help a third, or three men a fourth, more easily than one man, unaided, can help another. The benefits come out cheaper per capita.

The benefits I'm discussing here are the payments made to ex-partners or their families because of disability, retirement or death. To guarantee that these benefits will be paid, a three-man partnership contract can specify that the loss of one partner doesn't wash out the partnership. A lawyer is needed here. He can write the contract so that as long as two men remain, the partner-ship goes on, pledged to honor the original commitments. New partners, when admitted, must then accept those commitments.

Such a contract was written recently for three surgeons in

Virginia. They went further, though. They spelled out in the contract how the fringe benefits were to be earned and distributed. First, they agreed on three principles:

1. The partnership's income point system determines a partner's "rank." The three partners divided their joint earnings according to the point system I described in an earlier chapter. This establishes each partner's "rank." Dr. Delatour, who founded the practice, receives the maximum of 16 points. Dr. Griffiths, who's been with Dr. Delatour six years, also receives 16 points. Dr. Thurber is in his second year as a partner; he receives 12 points, with two two-point raises to come. Every month the net income of the practice is divided by the total points of all partners—44—to establish the value of one point.

2. Rank and length of service determine how long a partner receives benefits. The three partners agreed that the higher a partner's rank and the longer he serves the partnership, the longer he'll receive some income from partnership funds when his working days are over.

3. The partnership's earnings and a partner's allotted points determine how much he receives in benefits. It's obviously impractical to settle on actual dollar amounts when the contract is being drawn up. So the three partners have agreed to relate the size of the benefit checks to the partnership's income at the time the benefits are paid. They'll do this by assigning a greatly reduced number of points to the ex-partner and including him in their monthly division of income.

To show how these three principles work in practice, let's assume that one of the partners is forced out by permanent disability. A partner previously entitled to the maximum of 16 points will get a reduced income for two years from the remaining partners. But Dr. Thurber—who receives only 12 points—isn't left out. For his already-completed year as a junior partner, he's entitled to three months' benefits. By the end of this year, he'll be entitled to six months' benefits. Next year, nine months. And the year after, when he reaches the maximum of 16 points, he'll jump to two years' benefits like the others.

That's not all. For each year he receives the maximum number of points, a partner is entitled to six extra months of benefits. So if Dr. Delatour is disabled 10 years from now, his basic disability benefit will have risen by five years—six months for each completed year of work. He'll thus be entitled to monthly checks for seven years in case of permanent disability.

And there's still more to come. In recognition of Dr. Delatour's past work—remember, he founded the practice—his teammates have voted him two extra years of benefits. Dr. Griffiths' past service has been recognized by the award of one extra benefit year.

For the first five years that a disabled partner is entitled to benefits, his monthly check will be for the value of the reduced points —in this case two points. So if Dr. Delatour becomes ill and has to quit this year, his income points will be cut from 16 to two. As for the partners still practicing, Dr. Griffiths will still receive 16 points and Dr. Thurber 12, bringing the total number of points to 30. Drs. Griffiths and Thurber will divide each month's net by this figure and send Dr. Delatour two points' worth.

Right now, a point in this three-man partnership averages around $200 a month. The way things look, a $250 point is likely next year. And the partners believe that, as time goes on, the single-point value will rise still more. So they've agreed to step down the benefit points gradually. After five years on two points, a disabled partner will get (if he's earned it) five more years on one and a half points, five on one point, and five on one-half point. That's the end of the line.

So far, I've explained this partnership's plan in terms of permanent-disability benefits. But a partner can retire and get the same benefits. The three Virginia doctors have agreed as follows:

¶ First, a partner wishing to retire must give ample notice—in this case at least 60 days—so that his replacement can be recruited in good time.

¶ There'll be no pressure on any partner to retire before he's 65. But when he gets to that age, one of three things must happen: (1) He quits. (2) He's voted a continuance as a maximum-point partner on a year-to-year basis for five years at most. (3) He stays on but loses two points each year. At 70, he must drop out.

¶ Retirement benefits are exactly the same as the disability benefits. But if he continues working after 65, a partner won't add to his benefits. Delatour, now aged 49, can quit at 65 with 12 years' benefits coming (two years for being a maximum-point partner, eight years for the 16 years of work he'll do between now and then, plus two years extra for founding the practice). Griffiths, now 41, can get 15 years' benefits by working until he's 65 (two years for being a maximum-point partner, 12 years for the 24 years of work he'll do, plus one year for past service). Thurber, now 34, can qualify for a maximum of 16½ years' benefits (two years when he becomes a maximum-point partner at the age of 36 and 14½ years for the 29 years of work he'll do after that).

¶ If a retired partner dies before using up all the benefits he's entitled to, the checks will go to his widow. But they'll stop five years after her husband's death, even if his benefits haven't run out.

We now know what each partner can expect if he quits because of disability or advancing age. But what if one of them dies in harness? In that case, under their contract, the dead partner's beneficiary will draw his earned benefits for a maximum term of five years. (All three have named their wives as beneficiaries, with remainder to their children.) Thus, if a partner who's earned four years' benefits dies, his widow will get all he'd have received himself if he'd quit at that point. But if he dies with 10 years' credits, she'll get only five years' benefits.

The partners limit widows' benefits in this way because each partner has substantial life insurance. So each widow would be adequately provided for. On the basis of current earnings, five years' benefits would probably net her $24,000. They think that sum will square accounts generously.

It's understood, of course, that in exchange for all these benefits each partner surrenders his claim on the practice's accounts receivable. You can see why: A departing partner's accounts receivable furnish an important part of the cash with which to pay out his benefits.

One last feature of the three partners' plan remains. It isn't a fringe benefit in the true sense of the term. This feature was decided on because, at the final discussion before the contract was signed, young Dr. Thurber had a question:

"What if one of us pulls out voluntarily next week or next year? We've covered disability, retirement and death, but a man might just want to pack up and go. What then?"

"Good question," said the others. "Why can't our plan cover that possibility too?"

And so it does. If any one of the three decides to practice in California instead of Virginia, he simply gives at least 60 days' notice. Then he can head west and take with him whatever benefits he's earned. They'll be the same as if he were retiring with one restriction added: He'll have to settle beyond the confines of the county where his former partners practice. If he hangs out his shingle in the same county, he pays a penalty.

9.
Minimizing the partners' taxes

When two or more physicians form a partnership, still another party has an interest in the financial side of it: Uncle Sam. If you're not careful, you or your partner may end up paying him more than you'd expected. To keep his cut down to the legal minimum, take advantage of some provisions about partnerships in the tax law. For instance, you should know:

How to get all the depreciation deductions you're entitled to. Ordinarily, each partner shares in the depreciation deductions according to his interest in the earnings. For instance, if income is split down the middle, so are depreciation deductions. But sometimes the partnership agreement should specify a different way of splitting the deductions. Here are two cases of doctors who didn't have such a contract clause—and therefore lost money:

¶ Dr. Wilson, third man in a partnership, plunked down cash for a one-third interest in the partnership's depreciable property.

But his starting percentage of partnership income was only 20 per cent of the net. So he got only one-fifth of the first year's depreciation deduction. It was four years before he got a full third. He should have had a clause in his contract specifying that he get a third of the depreciation deductions right from the start.

¶ Dr. Johnson, equal partner with Dr. Willis, contributed property that cost $10,000. He'd already depreciated the property for tax purposes by $4,000, so its tax basis was $6,000. But a detail man assured him it was worth $8,000 on the market. The other partner, Dr. Willis, had no property, but he had $4,000 in cash. He gave it to Dr. Johnson to become half-owner of the property. As the years went by, he got depreciation deductions on $3,000 worth of assets, although he'd paid $4,000 for them. Dr. Willis should have insisted on a clause in the partnership contract specifying that he was to be credited with two-thirds of the annual depreciation deductions, since he'd paid two-thirds of the property's book value.

How to avoid being stuck for tax on a profit you never made. Drs. Barr and Burger, equal partners in a radiological practice, set up shop in a building contributed by Dr. Barr. It had cost him $30,000 many years previously, and its tax basis was down to $20,000. Dr. Burger contributed all the equipment. Its tax basis was $30,000, but since it was obvious that the equipment would wear out before the building did, he settled for a half interest in the joint assets.

The building didn't suit them, and inside a year they sold it. It brought $30,000—the same as its original cost but $10,000 above its book value. So there was a taxable gain of $10,000. Since nothing was said in their partnership contract about property sales, each co-owner was assessed a tax on $5,000. An angry Dr. Burger paid tax on a paper profit. Dr. Barr's gain was a real one.

The trap would have been eliminated if the Barr-Burger contract had said, "If contributed property is sold by the partnership, each partner shall be liable for all the tax on any unrealized gain on his contributed property accruing prior to the formation of this partnership."

How to get tax savings on property you bring into a partnership. When Drs. Newman and Sample teamed up, Dr. Newman contributed property that had cost him $5,000. He'd depreciated it by $3,000, so its tax basis was $2,000. Dr. Sample owned property that had cost him $9,000. He'd taken only $2,000 in depreciation deductions, so its book value was $7,000. But he decided not to contribute the property to the partnership because the partners wanted their property interests to be identical.

They could have evened things out if Dr. Newman had paid Dr. Sample $2,500—half the difference between the tax bases of their properties. But Dr. Newman said he could raise only $1,000. So Dr. Sample *sold* his property to the partnership for $2,000. Dr. Newman paid $1,000 to Dr. Sample as his half, and the new tax basis of the property became $2,000, the cost to the partnership.

Dr. Sample now had $1,000 from Dr. Newman and a tax-deductible loss of $5,000. In his tax bracket of 50 per cent, this loss was worth $2,500 in tax savings. Thus, Dr. Sample collected $3,500, and Dr. Newman's $1,000 bought him a half-share in Dr. Sample's costly equipment. Simple—and legal.

If a deal like this appeals to you, watch for two traps:

¶ Your loss on a sale of property to the partnership is not tax-deductible if your share of either profits or capital in the partnership is 51 per cent or more. So if you're on the long end of the partnership purse, don't sell any property to the partnership for a price below its tax basis.

¶ If you sell property to your partnership for more than its tax basis and your share in the partnership is more than 80 per cent, you don't get capital-gains treatment on the sale. Your profit is ordinary income, taxable in full. And under the newest tax rules, *any* gain over the property's Dec. 31, 1961, basis is considered ordinary income, no matter what your share of the partnership.

How to be sure of getting capital-gains treatment on a payment for goodwill. If goodwill isn't stipulated as a partnership asset, it doesn't exist and hence can't be sold.

Dr. Townsend, retiring from a three-man partnership, discovered that fact to his cost. His partners paid him $30,000 in all—$10,000 for his interest in partnership property, $10,000 for his interest in accounts receivable and $10,000 for goodwill. The first $10,000, being return of capital, wasn't taxable. The second $10,000 ranked as ordinary income. Dr. Townsend claimed capital-gains treatment on the third $10,000—and lost. The tax agent pointed out that there was no mention of goodwill anywhere in the partnership contract and that it hadn't ever been shown as an asset in any balance sheet. "It's ordinary income," he said, and it was.

If you think you might ever receive a goodwill payment, make sure you'll get capital-gains treatment by assigning a specific value to the goodwill when your attorney draws up your partnership agreement.

How to cut taxes on your "severance pay." If you take all that's due you in one lump when you pull out of your partnership, you can hoist your tax bracket sky high. Dr. Melton did just that. At the end of September he left a partnership from which he had already netted $36,000 that year. His property interest was $6,000, tax-free, and his partner offered him $18,000 for the receivables he was leaving behind. Dr. Melton took the total $24,000 in one lump sum. During the next three months, he netted $6,000 in another practice. That year he had outside income that exactly matched his exemptions and deductions, so his taxable income was $60,000 ($36,000 income from the partnership, plus $18,000 for his receivables, plus $6,000 from his new practice). And the taxes hurt.

With his partners' cooperation, Dr. Melton could have slashed his tax bill considerably. He could have used one of these two methods:

¶ He could have asked his partners to give him a paid leave of absence until he'd drawn the $18,000 for his receivables in regular monthly distributions. That way, he would have received part of the money in the next tax year.

¶ If his contract had allowed it, he could have taken the $18,000 over a long period of time. If he'd drawn, say, $500 a month for three years, his tax bill would have been much lower; Uncle Sam would have taxed him year by year on his annual receipts as he got them.

The provision needed in his contract: "The partnership's obligation to a withdrawing partner for accounts receivable may, with his consent, be liquidated by periodic payments on account of collections thereof, the amounts, frequency and number of such payments to be agreed upon at the time of his withdrawal."

There's one more tax trap to beware of: choosing one type of tax year for your partnership and another for yourself. Fortunately, it's not as easy to fall into this trap now as it was before the 1954 tax law was passed. Before 1954, many physicians who paid their personal taxes on a calendar-year basis fixed a different tax year—a fiscal year—for their partnerships. The object was to gain a deferment of taxes on the partnership's first 12 months of operations. The catastrophic consequence for some men: a bunching of from 13 to 23 months' earnings into one calendar year when a partner pulled out or died.

A case in point: Two North Carolina physicians paid their personal taxes on a calendar-year basis but had a February-through-January fiscal year for their partnership. One of the partners retired on Jan. 31, 1963, thus dissolving the partnership. Since the partnership ended during the 1963 calendar year, the doctor remaining in practice had to pay taxes on his income for the period of February, 1962, through January, 1963, as though he'd earned all of it in 1963. Although he netted only $33,000 during 1963, he paid taxes on $76,000. And in that bracket, the tax rate is pretty stiff.

It's still possible, although not easy, to convince the Internal Revenue Service that your partnership's fiscal year should be other than the calendar year. But I don't advise you to try, unless a tax expert can show you you'll be gaining benefits that outweigh the income-bunching risk I've mentioned.

Perhaps, as a member of an existing partnership, you're vulnerable to one or more of the tax dangers discussed here. If so, here's consolation: You can amend your contract so as to remove those dangers at any time before your tax return is due—even the day before. (You'll need I.R.S. approval to change your tax year, however.) And if you're still at the talking stage with a prospective partner, you'll feel better if you start the partnership off with a tax-tight contract.

10.

What to put in the contract

Not long ago I visited two pairs of prospective partners in cities 500 miles apart. One pair showed me an agreement they were about to sign. It consisted of a single sheet of legal-size paper. In the other city, the two partners-to-be handed me a 40-page agreement bristling with details. The 40-page contract prescribed exactly how a whole raft of unlikely disputes were to be solved, whereas the one-page contract left all problems to be solved as they cropped up.

When I raised a critical eyebrow at each document, the partners-to-be asked me what *should* go into a partnership agreement. First I stressed that whatever they ultimately decided must be checked by the best legal adviser available. Then I told them about a simple method I've often used to help doctors decide for themselves what to include and what to leave out of a contract. Some day you may want to try it yourself.

When you and another doctor are about ready to team up, make a list of disagreements that broke up the partnerships you've known. Then run down the list with your partner-to-be and ask yourselves which of these possible conflicts you want to cover in your contract. If there's disagreement as to whether a particular clause is needed, that's probably the very one you'd better put in. It's a dispute in the making.

High on your list of possible disputes to be covered by contract clauses will undoubtedly be division of income, apportionment of expenses, treatment of accounts receivable and various fringe benefits. I've already discussed those matters in earlier chapters, so there's no need to go over them again. But what about specifying such minutiae as time off? I don't advise it, though I recall this case

---

How to keep partnership contract disputes out of court

Partners with a mandatory-arbitration clause in their contract will probably never have to go to court about a partnership dispute. Some such clauses name a local judge, the clerk of the local superior court or a respected local attorney as an arbitrator. If you can't agree on a local man, you might ask the American Arbitration Association to supply one.

In either case, your arbitration clause could be worded along the lines of the association's standard clause:

"Any controversy or claim arising out of or relating to this contract, or the breach thereof, shall be settled by arbitration in accordance with the rules of the American Arbitration Association, and judgment upon the award rendered by the arbitrator[s] may be entered in any court having jurisdiction thereof."

The national headquarters of the association is at 477 Madison Avenue, New York 22, N.Y., and there are 19 regional offices spotted across the country.

---

of a partnership that did include a time-off clause when drawing up the contract:

Two pediatricians in partnership in a small county seat kept their office open Saturday afternoons for the convenience of farm families. Only one doctor was needed then, and for 20 years the same man kept Saturday afternoon hours while his partner, an older physician, played golf. When a young pediatrician joined the practice, this No. 3 man was allotted the Saturday duty—and he beefed loudly. No. 2 stood on his right to be relieved of Saturday duty. Junior finally accepted the assignment on the understanding that he'd inherit Saturday freedom when the senior partner retired in five years. This clause was solemnly written into the contract.

My feeling is, though, that if you can't solve time-off problems without a contract clause, maybe you shouldn't be planning a partnership at all.

There are many more significant questions that may lead to partnership disputes. Here are four such questions calling for specific answers in the partnership contract:

1. Who decides policy? Some otherwise smooth-sailing partnerships have been known to founder when situations like these arose:

¶ Dr. Middleton, partner of Dr. Frank, arrived at the office one morning and found a decorator busy in the reception room. "What gives?" he demanded. The decorator explained that Dr. Frank had called for a paint job. Dr. Middleton phoned his partner at the hospital and asked him what was going on. Responded Dr. Frank. "But yesterday you said yourself that the office could use a lick of paint." "So I did," snapped Dr. Middleton, "and you said our X-ray equipment was getting old. How'd you like it if I ordered a new machine on the strength of a casual remark you made?"

¶ Mary Waters, office nurse to Drs. Paine and Jones, asked Dr. Paine for a raise. He told her he'd discuss it with his partner— but then Dr. Paine went off on vacation. So Mary asked Dr. Jones about it herself, and he said: "Put yourself down for an extra $5 a week starting now." On his return Dr. Paine asked how come. Said Dr. Jones: "If you're going to fuss about $2.50, which is your weekly share of this $5 raise, I'm not at all sure that our partnership is worth the trouble."

¶ Dr. Mills hated house calls. If he couldn't talk the patient out of the idea, he'd go—at a high price. Several patients asked his 50-50 partner, Dr. Baron, why it cost so much more when Dr. Mills visited their homes. Dr. Baron's attempt to discuss the problem with his partner caused a blowup that ended their partnership.

Such blowups over policy decisions occur less frequently when one partner has a bigger stake in the practice than the other. There's a natural assumption of seniority in such partnerships. Sometimes this assumption is legalized by a contract clause that gives Senior the say-so when opinions differ. And occasionally the founder of a practice retains policy-making rights even after his partner has achieved 50-50 income status.

But more typically each man expects his view to count as much as his partner's. That's why, in practically every contract I've helped put together, there's a clause providing that all partners must O.K. hirings, firings and pay changes; new leases and contracts; new recurring expenses, however small; and one-shot expenditures over $25 or $50. (See sample clause on page 67.)

Three-man and four-man teams who want to turn over policy-making to one man may write the contract to vest all such powers in one partner. Some partnerships rotate the job among the partners, each taking a turn for a year. But I've found that a partnership is lucky if it has even one member who's willing and able to take on the full responsibility of decision-making.

2. *What about outside work?* Some partners neglect their practices for other income-producing activities. I remember a surgeon who had *seven* such moonlighting ventures. He was a partner in that many local businesses, active in the decision-making for all of them. His overworked surgeon-partner told me, "I sew up after

This contract clause tells who makes policy decisions

No personnel shall be hired or discharged, nor shall the pay of any employe be increased or reduced, nor shall any new recurring expenditure in any amount be authorized, nor shall any new nonrecurring expenditure in excess of $50 in any one transaction be authorized nor shall any decision materially affecting the policies or procedures of the partnership be put into effect except with the consent of [both/all] partners. The partners may delegate all these powers to one of their number for such period of time as they may determine if such action appears to them desirable.

EDITOR'S NOTE: *The partnership contract clauses shown here and on pages 68-70 are composite samples. Because they fit no real-life case exactly, they should not be adapted for actual use without legal advice.*

---

him and mind the store." This kind of situation can be nipped before it starts with a brief clause requiring partners to put the practice first. (See sample clause on page 68.)

3. How can you limit your financial liability? As far as partnership debts are concerned, you can't limit your liability. If damages of, say, $20,000 are awarded against your partnership and you're not covered by insurance, you and your 50-50 partner will each owe $10,000. In certain circumstances you could be stuck for much more. Suppose you paid your $10,000 and your partner couldn't pay his. All the partnership's assets—your share as well as his—might have to be sold to make up the amount due. And if the partnership assets didn't satisfy the debt, your personal property could be attached and sold.

Generally speaking, you won't be called on to redeem your partner's nonprofessional debts. But here again there's an "if." If your partner pledged his half of, say, the office X-ray equipment against a private loan and then the equipment had to be sold to satisfy the creditor, your half would go with it.

It's prudent, therefore, to write into your contract a flat prohibition of any unilateral pledging of the partnership's assets. Then if your partner does pawn the X-ray equipment, you'll at least be able to sue him for breach of contract and corresponding damages. (See sample clause on page 69.)

Some contracts even forbid partners as individuals to go surety for anyone, to co-sign notes or to guarantee in any other way the debts of third parties—even family members. I don't go along with that. Be content with preventing your associate from putting the partnership in hock.

4. How can you keep a former partner from becoming a competitor? Many an older physician has that question in the back of his mind when he imports fresh talent. He's heard of bright young men who, in two years of partnership, get cozy with the patients, leave the partnership and rent the vacant office across the street, taking the bulk of the practice's patients with them. To prevent such an occurrence, some contracts include a restrictive covenant— a clause barring an ex-partner from setting up a practice in the immediate area.

This contract clause restricts moonlighting

Each partner agrees to devote to the partnership practice his entire time and endeavor, and he will not, so long as the partnership exists, engage in any other gainful occupation requiring his personal attention without the written consent of the other[s]. This clause shall not restrict or prevent a partner from personally and for his own account investing or trading in stocks, bonds, securities, commodities or other forms of investment for his own benefit.

This contract clause limits liability among partners

Each partner hereby expressly agrees that he will not, except with the consent of the other[s], make, draw, accept or endorse any bill of exchange, promissory note, contract, lease or other engagement for the payment of money or its equivalent by this partnership nor pledge the credit of the partnership in any way whatsoever except as authorized under this agreement. And each partner agrees and covenants that any breach of this clause shall be sufficient ground for the other partner to terminate the partnership without notice or penalty.

A number of doctors become highly indignant when asked about restrictive covenants. One testy small-town surgeon snorted: "You think I'd really give a darn if Tom did quit and set himself up in practice next door? Any man who can make a living out of surgery at my expense is welcome to it!" And an internist whose partner had just died said, "I refused to sign a covenant when I joined Sam's practice, and I certainly won't try to impose a covenant on the man who takes Sam's place."

It's more usual, though, for opposition to a restrictive covenant to come from the new man in a partnership. Sometimes he gets mad at the implication that he might try to steal another doctor's patients. He often fails to see that the incumbent is only trying to protect himself.

Yet the ex-partner does have a case. If a covenant banishes him from the county, it can play hob with his life. He's probably been around long enough to own a home he likes. All his friends are local people. His wife is unhappy about the prospects of moving. His kids are in local schools. "Why," he asks himself, "should we all be uprooted simply because Fred and I have split up?"

What happens? Likely as not, he ignores the covenant and

sticks around. If his former partner asks a court to move him on, the judge may decide not to issue the order. The covenant-breaker can often show that the dissolution of the partnership wasn't completely his fault and that his former partner hasn't suffered any great income-loss. In some states, too, these restrictive covenants have been held to be "in restraint of trade" and, as such, judged to be unconstitutional.

For all these reasons I try to persuade doctors not to include covenants that require an ex-partner to leave town. Sometimes I meet a physician, however, who insists that his partner must be discouraged from competing with him if the partners should decide to call it quits on the partnership. Then I suggest that the contract be written to:

¶ Stipulate that when the ex-partner does compete locally, he is in fact damaging the practice he's left.

This contract clause discourages competition from an ex-partner

S econd party [the junior partner] hereby expressly agrees and covenants that, if he should voluntarily withdraw from this partnership and thereafter practice competitively, he will within 30 days of commencing competitive practice pay to first party [the senior partner] the sum of $10,000 as liquidating damages therefor under this agreement. But in the event he withdraws at the request of the first party or if the partnership is dissolved by mutual consent, he shall not be liable to pay such damages if he practices competitively. For the purposes of this agreement, the words "practices competitively" shall mean practicing his profession, by himself or with others, as principal, partner or employe within the county of Midstate during the 24-month period immediately following his withdrawal from this partnership.

¶ Arbitrarily fix a cash sum as compensation to be paid for such damage.

¶ Bind the withdrawing partner to pay this compensation if he competes locally.

If you decide to include such a clause in your contract, be reasonable. Don't try to send your ex-partner two states away. Generally, it's enough to bar him from your county. And don't send him into perpetual exile. If the contract prohibits him from practicing locally for two years, that should be enough. (See sample clause on page 70.)

11.

Dissolution clauses
to consider

"**F**or two years I watched Curt grind out his cigar butts in the instrument trays," a Midwestern internist told me with a shudder. "One day I decided that I couldn't stand it any longer. So I broke up the partnership."

A day later, the man he'd been talking about said to me: "Paul? He should wear an apron and carry a dustmop. Another month in his housewifely care and I'd have been taking my shoes off before I came in the office door."

About a week later I heard that a flourishing three-man pediatric team in Georgia had broken up because one man bit his nails. "Parents ask *us* how to cure children's nail-biting," mourned one of the pediatricians. "But we couldn't keep our own partner from gnawing his nails down to the knuckles."

Extreme cases? Not really. The obvious undesirables in a partnership—the drug addicts, alcoholics, chronic debtors and lazybones—are responsible for only a small number of partnership collapses. Far more numerous are the partnerships dissolved because the pasture that had looked so invitingly green turned out to be an acre of scrub. Listen to some of the reasons I've heard for partnership breakups in recent years:

¶ "I thought I'd learn something from a man who did so much surgery. When I found out it was bad surgery, I understood why I was his fourth partner in seven years."

¶ "Jason and I were equal in pay and in time off. But the way he arranged things, he had a country-club practice, and I had a welfare practice. I got tired of second-class status."

¶ "My big mistake was to team up with such a young man. I'm old-shoe myself, and he was as scientific as hell. It got so I couldn't take a fishing trip without losing some long-standing patient he'd irritated with his fancy tests."

¶ "The truth is, I got sick of haggling over who was hired, who was fired and who got a $5 raise. We had a summit meeting about every little thing."

¶ "Joe was just fine. Couldn't have wished for a better partner. But his wife and mine couldn't hit it off."

If you're thinking of going into partnership, you may be confident that you and your prospective partner won't have any of those problems. Chances are you're right. But remember, none of the physicians I've quoted expected things to turn out as they did. That's why it's sensible to make a few key decisions *before* you sign a partnership agreement. Otherwise, you might find—as others have—that two men who team up with the friendliest feelings can quarrel bitterly over the terms of their separation.

It's been my experience that you can take a lot of the acrimony out of a partnership dissolution by asking the following questions and then writing the answers into the partnership agreement:

How much notice shall we give? When a partnership is dissolved by mutual consent, it can, if desired, end on the spot. In one instance I know of, a physician flew out of the office after a disagreement and sent a friend around later for his medical bag and his desk set. But such instantaneous cutoffs are rare. Usually the proposal to dissolve originates with one partner, who suggests that things be wound up at some convenient early date.

Most partners find that 30 days' notice is enough. But notices of 60 and even 90 days aren't unusual. There's a lot to be said for a reasonably long notice: It's easier on the patients. It gives the partners a breathing space they can use to plan their next moves. It allows time for tidying up financial affairs. And I've known it to give a trigger-tempered partner time to back down.

If you include in your contract a clause requiring notice of desire to dissolve, add this useful proviso: "Provided that this notice may be waived, in whole or in part, by the partner receiving it, at the request of the partner tendering it, but not otherwise." Such a proviso protects a partner against being told: "Finish in 30 days, hell! We're finished *now*. Get your stuff out today."

Who gets the office? Since an established address and phone number are advantageous to the man who can keep them, the office can be a big bone of contention when both partners are staying in town. If one partner had the office first, he usually gets to stay in it. If it was specially rented for joint practice, a tie-breaking procedure may be needed if the contract is silent on the subject. Here's the way the problem was solved in three cases I know of:

¶ Two Tennessee partners flipped a coin for the right to stay in an office they'd leased for a term of years.

¶ Two Ohio men, each adamant that the other shouldn't get a jump on him, sublet their office to a new man in town.

¶ Two New York City specialists settled for alternate days in the office they'd leased as partners.

Not all partners reach a calm and fair decision about the office. One Texas surgeon refused to vacate the partnership office and held up the arrival of his successor for four months. Backed by a smart attorney, the departing surgeon then pocketed $2,000 for relinquishing his interest in a lease that still had two years to go.

The wise thing to do: Decide before you sign the contract who'll be using the office door key after the ball is over.

What happens to the equipment, furnishings and supplies? Assume the whistle has blown on your partnership. You're staying; he's leaving. The bank account and the office cash have been divided. Now, do you keep all the office equipment, furnishings and supplies, or does he ship some of them to his new location? If the latter, do you tour the premises together, dealing out items by the one-for-you-and-one-for-me method?

The man who's leaving rarely takes the tangible assets with him lock, stock and barrel, but I saw it happen once. They were taken in part-payment of a debt owed by the man who kept the office. Nor is it customary to parcel out the property, though I've known a few men to claim their shares. Sometimes a man will hold out for a few favorite items: a chair he likes or some instruments. I remember one doctor who took an adding machine and nothing else.

In most cases it's simpler for the partner keeping the office to keep the equipment, furnishings and supplies. If it's an equal partnership at the time of the split and he owns only one-half of the tangibles, he'll need to buy the other half.

To fix the sale price, some partners call in an appraiser—usually an equipment salesman. Yet many partners find they can agree on a figure without outside help. If their accountant has prepared regular balance sheets, they don't have much trouble. Many doctors used to settle for book value—the depreciated value of the property as shown on the partnership's books for tax purposes. But now that tax regulations permit faster write-offs, book value isn't a good way to fix the sale price. A Massachusetts G.P. named Alfred Knorr recently found that out.

When Dr. Knorr joined Dr. Martin Payson in partnership, he bought a half-interest in Dr. Payson's tangible assets for $3,000— their book value. He agreed that, if he left, he'd sell back his property interest "at book." Then he went halves with his partner in the purchase of $10,000 worth of new equipment, which they began to depreciate the fastest way possible. They claimed the initial 20-per-cent-of-cost first-year allowance and chose the double-declining-balance method of writing off the remaining 80 per cent of cost.

Dr. Knorr left the partnership a little more than a year later. By that time, book value had nose-dived. He'd laid out $8,000. He got back $5,900. His loss wasn't tax-deductible, nor was Dr. Payson's gain taxable.

Before you stipulate book value as the selling basis, I suggest you ask a tax expert to study the details of your purchases and write-off methods.

What happens to the medical records? Here again, if one partner is heading for distant parts, the answer is easy: The medical records stay put. But if both men are going to be around town, records can be a subject of bitter dispute. When partners have alternated freely in the care of patients, the question of which man has the major interest in a chart can be highly arguable. Some solutions I've seen:

¶ One partner had joined the other's established practice. When the partnership was dissolved, all the records remained with the founder.

¶ A surgeon had a larger interest in partnership income and property than another. The one with the larger interest kept all the records.

¶ Two equal partners had set up a general practice from scratch. They agreed that the man who had first seen a given patient would be the one to get that patient's record.

¶ Two internists traded one chart against another, as they judged their patients' probable preferences. When some patients proved them wrong—by showing up at the other man's office—the doctor with the chart turned it over to his ex-partner.

¶ Two G.P.s invited all their patients to choose between them and divided their medical records accordingly.

¶ When two pediatricians broke up, the man who kept the office kept all the original records, and the man who moved across town took photocopies with him.

The best way? There isn't one. What to do with the medical records is something you have to talk over—and it's a good idea to do the talking while you're still firm friends.

What do we do about unpaid accounts? A Florida internist has been receiving occasional small checks from doctors in New York and Pennsylvania for years. He'd been in partnerships in both states before he went South. The checks represent his share of the money his former partners are still collecting on old accounts.

Passing along the cash as it dribbles in is still the favorite way of liquidating an ex-partner's interest in accounts receivable. But you don't have to do it that way. Look at these three options, all used by doctors who prefer to clear things up faster:

¶ The limited-time method: The departing man gets his full share of the collections that come in after he's left, for a specified time. After a year, say, his checks stop. He loses some money from later collections—but probably not much, unless the practice was one with a lot of liability insurance cases. As orthopedists know, some of these pay off very late.

¶ The bargain sale: The partner who's leaving gets a lump sum, which is arrived at by negotiation. One partner asks, "What'll you take for your receivables?" and the other counters with, "What'll you give?" Later, the man who stays on can keep all he collects from patients. Who wins and who loses depends on the bargain that's struck. I know a surgeon who sold his half-interest in $50,000 worth of accounts receivable for $5,000. But he was in a hurry to go, for reasons unconnected with medicine.

¶ Sale by formula: The man who stays buys the other's interest in the partnership's unpaid accounts, using this formula: R minus U minus L minus C times S.

R is the total amount of the unpaid balances on the patients' account cards.

U is the amount deemed uncollectible. This can be an area of dispute. Sometimes the head of a local collection agency is called in to advise.

L is a deduction for normal collection losses. Ten per cent is usually considered fair.

C is the estimated cost of collecting and forwarding the money. Here also, 10 per cent is reasonable.

S, the multiplier, is the seller's percentage of interest in the partnership income at the time he leaves.

Suppose the unpaid bills of the Brown-Green partnership add up to $40,000. The doctors agree that accounts totaling $10,000 are so old as to be worthless. They cut the remaining $30,000 by $3,000 for collection losses and by $3,000 for collection costs. That leaves $24,000. Dr. Green, a 50 per cent partner, is leaving. Dr. Brown pays him $12,000 for his interest in the receivables and keeps all he collects on the joint accounts.

A junior partner will sometimes make this agreement: If the partnership is dissolved before he reaches full rank, he'll forfeit all claims on receivables. That can be hard on a man who's paid cash down for an interest in the receivables, rather than buying in on installments. And a man who hasn't been required to buy in at all may or may not be out of pocket, depending on whether the receivables are higher or lower when he leaves than when he joined and how much of them he personally put on the books.

You sometimes come across a doctor who's shrewd about receivables. I know of a young surgeon who joined a partnership that had receivables of $73,000. He wasn't required to buy into them. When his income share stood at 20 per cent, he gave notice and claimed one-fifth of the unpaid accounts, which were then $80,000. His partners argued that at best he was entitled to $1,400 —20 per cent of the $7,000 added while he was with them. But to avoid a threatened suit, they paid him $5,000. It was just as well they did; they probably would have lost the suit. A carelessly worded clause in their partnership agreement said: "A withdrawing partner shall be entitled to a share in the accounts receivable corresponding to his percentage of net income at the time of his withdrawal."

For every shrewd partner, though, there are many like the Maryland G.P. who told me: "Steve charged me nothing for the receivables when I came in, and that's exactly what I'm taking out. I've been well-paid."

Which method of dividing receivables do I favor? Sale by formula. And for a man who's joining a going practice without buying in, make this adjustment: Multiply S (his income percentage) by the percentage of increase in the receivables made during the life of the partnership. In the Brown-Green example

---

How to handle a potential practice-wrecker

If you find that your partner is dragging down your practice, call off all bets. And do it fast. Cutting office paychecks won't cure the all-too-common foot-dragger or the rarer drug addict, alcoholic or chronic debtor. Your key word with them is "Good-by."

The partnership agreement can help you say that parting word if it outlaws halfhearted effort, unethical professional conduct and undesirable personal behavior, as does the following sample clause:

"Each partner hereby pledges his active and industrious efforts in the practice of his profession in the interest of the partnership; his faithful adherence to all recognized professional ethics and customs; and his careful avoidance of all acts, habits and usages that might injure in any way, directly or indirectly, the professional reputation and standing of the partnership or any partner. And each partner agrees and convenants that any breach of this pledge shall be sufficient ground for the innocent partner or partners to terminate the partnership without penalty and that the offending partner shall forfeit any and all claim to benefits otherwise herein provided."

---

given above, suppose that Dr. Brown's receivables had stood at $30,000 when Dr. Green joined his practice. Then if the partners' combined receivables were $40,000 when Dr. Green left, the increase would have been 33⅓ per cent. So when he left, Dr. Green would have been due only $4,000—one sixth of $24,000.

After all this discussion of the ins and outs of partnership practice, you've probably got some concrete ideas about how a partnership should be set up. You may even be saying to a partner-to-be, "Let's shake on it." Shake hands, by all means—but don't leave it at that. Your agreement should be written, signed, witnessed and, preferably, registered. So call in your attorney.

Tell him every detail of what you've agreed. Ask him to check that everything will hold up under Federal, state and local law. Ask him if you're headed for tax trouble. Listen carefully to any ideas he has for calking possible leaks. If your contract provides benefits for widows, he may suggest that your respective wives attest the contract.

Finally, when you get your copy of the completed document, lock it away in a safe place. When will you next see it? Not, I hope, until you haul it out to show the new man who's planning to join your thriving team.

Part **II**

*Seven doctors report their personal
experiences in selecting good potential partners,
saying no to bad ones, testing
partnership before committing themselves,
getting patients used to the idea and
trying other varieties of
combined practice.*

12.

My prelude to partnership

By Carlyle Grady, M.D.

After nearly eight years of solo practice in the Southwest, I was dog-tired. The load was just too big for one man, and the idea of taking an associate was becoming more and more appealing.

It wasn't just the lure of a reduced workload and more leisure. The experience of an OBG-friend pointed up two additional attractions. "My patients get faster and better service," he told me, "and my income is a lot higher than it would have been if I'd stayed solo."

It sounded good, but I knew there could be drawbacks, too. Several of my colleagues had broken off with associates after a tryout of a year or so. The G.P. in the next block complained: "The man I took on worshiped lab tests. I couldn't teach him my kind of medicine." Another told me: "Patients who were used to my ways didn't like being fobbed off on a less experienced man." And a neurologist underlined a problem that hadn't occurred to me: "We might have hit it off if his wife had only kept her nose out of our business affairs."

The combined experience of my colleagues made one thing clear: I'd have to tackle certain basic questions *before* I took on an associate. So I listed the questions I considered most important (see below).

Having pretty well decided to take the plunge, I had to find my man. From the start, I'd liked the looks of Joe Bishop, a resident at our hospital. I'd been watching his work for nearly a year. He seemed to have energy, enthusiasm and a forthright personality. His ability was proven, and there was no cockiness about him. I felt that my experience—plus the fresh ideas he'd soaked up in his recent training—would make a hard-to-beat combination.

Well, there seemed to be nothing in *his* personality to frighten me—but what about mine? Had eight years in solo practice made me too set in my ways? After a bit of soul-probing, my honest

---

Want an associate? Take this quiz first

1. Is my prospective associate reasonably mature and flexible—and am I?
2. Are we personally compatible?
3. Are we medically compatible?
4. What salary should I offer?
5. What inducements, besides salary, can I offer?
6. What kind of agreement should we have at the outset?
7. Will I need another aide? If so, part time or full time?
8. How much office space and equipment will I have to add?
9. How will I educate my patients to accept the new man?
10. To what extent will my associate and I—and our wives—see each other socially?

---

conclusion was that I was going to have to give a little to get along with an associate.

The question of our medical compatibility didn't worry me. Having observed young Bishop, I felt that our clinical opinions were likely to jibe in most cases. When they didn't, I was sure we'd have enough tact to keep our disagreements from the patient. I remembered one young associate who'd confided to me: "When we alternate on a case, the patient is apt to say: 'You tell me one thing and Dr. Brown tells me another. How am I supposed to know who's right?'"

I realized Bishop was anxious to earn a decent living. He'd borrowed to finish his training, and he already had two kids. Could I make my proposition attractive to him?

I sampled physicians in my area and found that a starting salary of $12,000 for an associate was about right. But could I afford it?

My practice was netting $29,000 a year before taxes. My income from other sources just about covered my exemptions and personal deductions, so that $29,000 was all taxable. If I paid Bishop $12,000—assuming that he didn't pull in an extra nickel of office income—my taxable income would be cut to $17,000. But my tax would be reduced by at least $4,730. Uncle Sam would, in effect, be paying nearly 40 per cent of Bishop's salary. The actual cost to me would be $7,270.

But what about growth? My net was then increasing at an annual rate of $2,000. With Bishop to cover for me on certain evenings, on weekends and during vacation time, I could take on more patients. And he'd certainly attract some, too. So I decided that Bishop, for $12,000, was a good investment. How did my proposition strike him?

He liked it fine. The salary, he said, was acceptable, but he was even more interested in the long-term financial outlook.

I then offered the next arrangement I'd had in mind: If our gross in the first year exceeded my current gross by more than his salary—and if we could get along with each other—I'd take him as a partner. If these conditions were not met, we planned to try another year of association. In the first year of partnership he'd get 30 per cent of our net income, and the figure would rise progressively until it reached 50 per cent after five years. Bishop accepted.

I'd already been warned by other doctors: "Put your terms of association in writing!" And Bishop and I agreed we wanted no misunderstandings. I called in a management consultant to check our plan out in detail and then had a lawyer draft the contract.

The formal agreement took note of such items as time off (including vacations and sick leave), auto allowances, access to drug samples and payment of Bishop's liability insurance policies. It also contained a statement of intentions looking toward a future partnership.

I also agreed to hire a lab technician, going along with Bishop's suggestion that we beef up the lab facilities and acquire an X-ray machine. He'd convinced me that, with two of us, this would be a good investment.

Our contract signed, Bishop finished his residency while I built a new wing onto my office to accommodate him. If our venture flopped, I reasoned, I could always rent the space.

My willingness to make all these additional investments was prompted by the unhappy experience of a G.P.-friend. "I didn't see the point of all this costly expansion until my associate and I had been through our year's tryout," he'd told me. "Now, it seems perfectly obvious that my failure to add personnel, office space and equipment doomed our tryout. Our office wasn't big enough to handle the traffic we attracted, so some of it fell off. The equipment wasn't enough to go around when we were both working, and so the patients—and we—had to wait. Soon, we were losing patients. If I ever take on another associate, I'll make sure we have plenty of room, equipment and help."

Taking still another tip from a colleague, I found the hospital a good place to begin introducing my patients to my associate.

For the first four months we made rounds together. Soon I was able to transfer some of these patients to him. I also made it a point to have Bishop meet each patient in my office during the first few months. This courtesy not only flattered the patient but enhanced Bishop's prestige. And when I felt he was pretty well oriented, I deserted him for a three-week vacation.

By the time I returned, many of my patients had come to like him. Some even sent their families and friends to see him, not me. I feel this opportunity for patients to select from two personalities gives our practice a strength it lacked when I was working solo.

How did my plunge into additional investment work out? We've done enough routine X-ray work by now to pay for the machine, and our lab girl's work lets us diagnose while the patient is still in the office. I no longer hear patients grumbling about having to make a separate trip to the hospital for an X-ray or a c.b.c. But best of all, handling this work under one roof seems like better medicine. And as for the extra wing, I don't know how we could have handled our rising case load without it.

Bishop and I began our association over three years ago, when I was netting $29,000. This year our net before taxes will run about $65,000—$26,000 for him, $39,000 for me (we're on a 60-40 basis now). What's more, I'm not nearly as tired nowadays as I used to be on my smaller income.

What did we do about social get-togethers? Bishop and I were in solid agreement on this. We decided at the start that our wives should be completely informed about all provisions of our contract. Next, we resolved that neither wife should be permitted to dabble in the office operation. Lastly, we made up our minds to go easy on family social contacts. We felt we could limit our four-somes to one or two functions a year, for Bishop and I agree that we see quite enough of each other all day long. It's refreshing to have other faces to brighten our evenings!

So what's the secret of my success in finding and keeping an associate? I can sum it up in one word: preparation.

13.

How I found the right partners

By Robert C. Hopkins, M.D.

"How long will things go on like this?" my wife asked me tearfully one Wednesday night a couple of years ago. How do I know it was a Wednesday? Because no local doctor was likely to be found in his office on a Wednesday. None, that is, except me.

When I started practice here in Lake City, Pa., about nine years ago, the older physicians thoughtfully referred their Wednesday and Sunday emergency calls to me. Seven years later, they were still giving me this friendly boost, though my need for it was long past. The area we served was growing, and every doctor in it was straining under a heavy patient load. Then, too, the older M.D.s weren't getting any younger; young M.D.s weren't being drawn to this rural section; and the nearest hospital was 16 miles away.

Thus, overwork was my daily portion, but Wednesday and Sundays were particularly harrowing. They held special terrors for my wife, too. Looking at her tearful face that night, I realized what she'd been through—trying to cook, housekeep, rescue our three youngsters from countless crises and play my assistant on a constantly busy phone. It was then I knew I really had to buckle down and find myself a partner—or else pull up stakes.

For some time, I'd been dreaming of taking on a young colleague to lighten the load. But the prospects of getting one weren't too bright. All the capable young M.D.s seemed to head for the big cities and suburbs as soon as they'd completed their interneships or residencies. And since most of the partnerships that *had* been started in this area had eventually broken up, friends and colleagues had urged me to forget the idea. But that night my wife and I devised a plan.

Today, thanks to that plan, I'm teamed up with two other doctors, and we do a thriving general practice in a smart new medical center. We give our area coverage 24 hours a day, seven days a week. Yet vacations and days off are no problem. Hospital visits and night calls—once a daily occurrence when I was alone—now come up every third day. My wife's spirits have blossomed in her new-found freedom, and my residence has become a real *home*.

How did I do it? Thinking about those partnerships that had foundered, I decided that their failure could be blamed on one glaring oversight: The partners had never taken the trouble to find out how they and their families would get along together. I resolved to avoid that mistake. As I see it, *compatibility* is the element contributing most to a successful partnership. Here, then, is the six-point plan my wife and I drew up that night:

1. Find out if the area really needs another physician. This called for a study of the doctor-patient ratio in our area, comprising Lake City and neighboring Girard. Using the rough gauge of one M.D. for every thousand people, I came up with an unexpected finding: We needed not one but at least *two* more doctors. Considering that most of our local physicians were growing older and limiting their practices, there was no doubt about it. I had to double my effort.

2. *Locate a prospective partner.* Actually, I'd aready been looking for several years. And I now had my eye on four or five likely
internes at our local hospital over in Erie. But I knew I'd have to
move fast if I wanted to catch two good men. Through observation and interviews, I finally narrowed my choice to two doctors
who were planning to form their own partnership. When I offered
them the chance to join a more experienced man, they seemed
interested enough. After setting a date for them to pay me a visit,
I went to work on the next step:

3. *Rough out a specific program for setting up the partnership.*
My feeling was that we should function as a unit, using our group
name on letterheads and bills but keeping collections separate. Full
partnership, if we eventually decided we really wanted it, could
come later. But initially, one of us would be available for house
calls each day, another would make hospital rounds, and the third
would be free of these responsibilities for that day. Income from
all hospital work would be shared by all. My present equipment
would be available to my two colleagues, but they would share the
cost of maintenance and of new equipment as needed. Salaries and
office expenses would likewise be shared.

Office space posed more of a problem. How could we all make
use of my existing office—a 1,000-square-foot facility I'd added to
my home four years ago—without having the newcomers on top
of my family? I'd managed to become quite handy at carpentry
over the years, and it really paid off here. At my drawing board,
I worked out a plan to detach the office intact, move it to an
adjacent lot and add 2,000 square feet to it. Each physician would
then have three complete examining rooms, plus shared rooms for
special examinations, physiotherapy, X-rays, etc. The basement
would house a complete laboratory. All told, the building and
equipment would represent an investment of about $50,000.

4. *Give your partnership candidates the straight facts.* As the
day of our meeting approached, two questions kept nagging me:
(1) How could I sell these two talented young doctors on the at-

tractions of a practice in Lake City, Pa.? (2) What if they moved in only to find later they didn't like it? It was clearly in my own interest as well as theirs to be as comprehensive and objective as possible in giving the facts. So I mimeographed two lists. One itemized both the advantages and disadvantages of working in the area (see below). The other documented the community's need for two more physicians. When Dick Boyle and Dick Rahner arrived, I handed them these lists and suggested they discuss them at home with their wives.

Then I took them on a tour of my office. I opened record books

---

Pros and cons of a three-docto

Advantages

1. Chance to be a partner of experienced G.P. who knows area.
2. Chance to join an established, centrally located practice.
3. Chance to practice in an area that needs G.P.s as shown by study.
4. Ample, modern office facilities.
5. Increased time off under rotation system of three-man group.
6. Lower over-all operating costs (salaries, services, etc.).
7. Excellent highways to nearby city of 160,000 people, with two open-staff hospitals.
8. Approval by local leaders of establishment of group.
9. Relatively low living costs.
10. Real estate values lower than in city, favoring early purchase of home.
11. A progressive, growing community, with a diversity of income (farming, industrial, etc.).
12. Adequate school, church and fun facilities; Lake Erie in your backyard.
13. Pleasant, homey atmosphere of a small town.

and gave them a clear picture of my income, collection ratio, expenses, etc. That evening, I let them sample my wife's cooking at dinner. Later, we met with some Chamber of Commerce representatives who gave the young M.D.s a glowing but factual account of the area's coming expansion. New industries were moving in, they said, and new families were sure to follow.

The meeting was a success. The two M.D.s seemed to be impressed, and the C. of C. men were obviously delighted with the prospect of having around-the-clock medical coverage. They offered to back the project to the limit.

---

artnership in Lake City, Pa.

Disadvantages

1. All the dangers of an experiment, being first three-man group in wide area.
2. Lower fees than in city.
3. Greater responsibility because of distance from consultants and hospital.
4. Delay in return of reports, etc., from hospital and consultants because of distance factor.
5. Demand to perform office and home deliveries, still popular in this area.
6. More driving necessary because of large area covered (e.g., hospital 16 miles away in area of large snow deposits), with higher gas and car-operating costs and more time loss.
7. Less active association with other doctors because of relative isolation.
8. Possible opposition to the group by doctors in area.
9. Lack of live theater, orchestras, ballet, art galleries, etc.
10. Possible adverse reactions in the community to the project—because it's new.
11. The disadvantages found in any small town—e.g., living under the public eye.

Meanwhile, something equally important was taking place: We doctors were discovering that we liked each other. And so we arranged to take what I considered the most crucial step in my master plan:

5. Make sure that all concerned are mutually compatible. We began with a cookout at my summer cottage, where our wives became enchanted with each other's children. There were eight of them—all rather small and, as the day wore on, rather fretful. Yet our wives sailed through this test with aplomb.

It turned out that Pat Boyle was a genius at organizing games; Wilma Rahner was a fine storyteller. We discovered a number of mutual interests besides medicine and children—water sports, for one. And so we arranged for two more compatibility tests: a fishing trip for parents only, and a boating-swimming excursion for all 14 of us.

The fishing trip a week later gave us a chance to talk college, Kierkegaard and local politics. By the time the third outing rolled around, the youngsters seemed to take it for granted that we were one big clan. Soon my wife, with a new mission in life, began house-hunting for our new friends. As a final test, I began to introduce the Boyles and the Rahners into the community. The three of us visited other doctors in the vicinity. We attended community functions together with our wives. We went to the medical society dances.

At all these affairs, we made it quite clear that we were thinking of going into partnership. This invariably drew us an enthusiastic response—quite the opposite of what I'd expected—and several of my friends privately congratulated me on the men I'd chosen as prospective colleagues.

"They're just right for our town," a young woman patient of mine said. "You were lucky to find them." We actually spent more time getting to know each other than we did discussing money or the new building and equipment.

All told, our compatibility testing lasted more than a month.

And while this heavy socializing made demands on my time, Drs. Boyle and Rahner now agree with me that it was time well spent. The next step was easy:

6. *Sign him up.* At this point, I was able to ask each prospective partner flatly, "How about a contract?" We immediately agreed on terms along the lines of my early proposals. I had my lawyer draw up the papers. Before we all signed, both men went over them with their own lawyers.

With our arrangement legally established, we now began to work out details. My office was detached from my house and towed to the adjacent lot; our new building began to take shape around it. Much of the equipment we installed—built-in cabinets and folding desks, for example—was designed to save space and increase our efficiency. An electronic phone-answering device we purchased announces the name and number of the doctor on call as well as the home numbers of the other doctors.

To maintain our individual practices and, at the same time, consolidate bookeeping, we bought an accounting machine. This labor-saver can record all patient-services and code the ledger cards with a symbol for each doctor. In this way, group charges are kept on a single card that provides a breakdown for each physician to bill his own patients. Our three-doctor, four-girl medical center has become a source of pride to the community. Real estate agents routinely stop to show prospective homeowners the attractive building and to impress them with the service it symbolizes. And our patients are delighted: They feel free to choose their own doctor, and in an emergency they're glad to see whichever man happens to be on call.

My colleagues and I have many reasons to be pleased. The arrangement has proved economically sound. For example, our present office space for three, with all-day and evening aide coverage, costs only 10 per cent more to maintain than my old facility for one, which was covered only during my office hours.

The service we give is unquestionably more efficient than what

I could give before, and the increased leisure I now enjoy is priceless. I suspect the most appreciative person in town is my wife. Ethel finally gets some of the pampering she's deserved for so long. And she's thriving on it.

The friends and colleagues who once warned me against a partnership have nothing but encouragement for our present plan to bring in a dentist. So we're going to do that—just as soon as we find the right man. We've already interviewed two promising candidates—but they failed to pass that compatibility test.

14.

Why I said no to eight prospective senior partners

By Dale Wickham, M.D.

Even before finishing my residency in pediatrics, I decided I was cut out for combined practice with a well-established older man. I wanted to locate in New England. I also wanted a working arrangement that would eventually lead to a 50-50 partnership. Aside from meeting these basic requirements, my only problem was finding the right man to team up with. Soon a stint as an Air Force physician gave me enough time off to investigate the possibilities.

When I started looking, I found myself in a seller's market. Some doctors were actually bidding against each other for my services. After weeding out several offers that obviously fell short of my basic requirements, I had nine proposals left to consider—and almost a year in which to choose among them while completing my military service.

During the year, I visited each man in the revealing setting of his own office. I'm glad I took the trouble. By doing so, I was able to avoid some unhappy partnership situations I might otherwise have become involved in. My final decision against eight of the nine offers was based on some pretty strong objections. These were the danger signals as I saw them:

The scut-work syndrome. "I'm looking for a man who's not afraid of work," said Doctor No. 1 in opening a lecture on the "crop of softies" that medical schools and hospitals are turning out today. His lecture concluded with these words: "I want a doctor, not a clock-watching union man." I didn't have to probe deeply to find out what those words actually meant. That doctor wanted an indefatigable junior partner who would devote himself to handling all the senior's weekend work, long-distance house calls and night calls.

At least he intended to pull his own load in the office. Doctor No. 2 indicated that he wouldn't do even that. He was strong on yachting, hunting and golf—far stronger on those than on the practice of medicine. It became clear that he was looking for someone to mind the store while he relaxed. I visualized an office with an absentee senior in a so-called joint practice that couldn't grow enough to provide a decent income for either of us. Maybe he didn't need the money, but I did. And covering for him all the time would leave little leisure time for myself.

Don't get me wrong. I'm not afraid of hard work. But I do think patient relations suffer when all the work is dumped on one man. Patients don't want a mere substitute or a chore boy looking after their health needs. They want somebody who counts.

Believing this, I backed off fast when I spotted the next danger signal:

The condescension complex. We hadn't even discussed my training, board certification or professional work in the Air Force when Doctor No. 3, in his 50s, assured me: "After you've been around this office awhile, you'll forget a lot of that lab medicine they taught you in the hospital. A good doctor uses his God-given senses. When you're as far along as I am, you can tell what disease a patient has by the smell he gives off." He went on like that for the better part of an hour, reminding me of a Vermont farmer I once knew: He wore out his land needlessly and died broke, still giving vent to his endless scorn of "book larnin'."

Despite that doctor's lecture, I still believe that medicine is more science than smell. I also believe that it's bad policy for an older doctor to treat a young colleague as if he were still a medical student. That, in effect, is what Doctor No. 4, also in his 50s, started doing as soon as we'd met.

"When you have a choice of therapy, son, don't worry about it," he said. "Just ask me." Later, in front of a patient: "Take a look at these tonsils, son, and tell me what *you'd* do." And finally, in front of his aide: "I think I have a place for you here, son—a place where you can grow." Instead of staying to grow, I'm afraid I decided to go—fast.

Still another doctor made me feel small through no fault of his own. The danger signal was this:

A reputation no newcomer could live up to. I was truly excited and flattered, as any young doctor would be, when Doctor No. 5 made me a partnership offer. He was nationally known and would obviously have a lot to teach me. I had no doubts about wanting to join him—until I happened to overhear the following conversation at his receptionist's desk:

AIDE (to a patient's mother): You'll be sure to follow Doctor's diet instructions to the letter?

MOTHER: Don't worry! To me, that man is God. If he told me to throw my baby in the lake, I'd go ahead and do it without thinking twice.

This man, I realized, was worshiped by the people he served. How would they feel if they called him in an emergency and I showed up instead? Cheated, of course. It would take years for me to build up a following of patients who trusted me. Working in the shadow of his reputation was too much to ask of any young doctor. I wanted a better chance of establishing my own identity and of keeping busy on my own merits. I reluctantly decided against Doctor No. 5.

My next prospective senior partner, Doctor No. 6, did offer me a chance to develop my own identity and get plenty of professional satisfaction. But one vital ingredient was missing. Here's the danger signal that warned me off:

A practice without enough earning power to support two. Doctor No. 6 had his office in a town with a near-indigent population. It had been a one-industry town, but the mill that had provided the paychecks had moved away. Most of this doctor's patients were on welfare now. That meant small fees or no fees and more paper work than he'd ever be paid for. Because other doctors had sized up the economic situation and were leaving town, his patient load had nearly doubled, but his net income had risen only slightly. Though I sympathized with his situation, I felt no desire to be part of it.

Nor was it practical for me to try. His was a one-man office, and he didn't have the money to expand. That points up another danger signal:

Not enough space for a partner. This problem wasn't unique to Doctor No. 6, who had all the welfare patients. The professional facilities of Doctor No. 7 were so cramped that we couldn't have had office hours at the same time. Yet he saw no need to get more space until a year's tryout justified the investment. Without adequate facilities, that tryout would be doomed. Our joint practice could hardly grow when there was no space for treatment of additional patients.

I think my experience with that potential partner helps explain this final danger signal:

No spelling out of partnership details. Doctor No. 8 disappointed me on this score. He was willing to sign a contract right away—so long as it contained nothing but our financial agreement. When I asked him about such matters as liability insurance, auto allowance, vacations and sick leave, he dismissed them all with this suggestion: "Let's not be so formal. We can work out these things as we go along."

I didn't agree. At this early stage of my career, I couldn't afford a false start. I had to know exactly what I was getting into. There was no need for my first trial to fail because of disagreement over some matter that could have been spelled out in the contract. I preferred teaming up with a man who'd try in every reasonable way to make our trial run a success.

I found such a man in Doctor No. 9—Ford Rainey. Though Dr. Rainey was 20 years my senior, he obviously felt that my exposure to the latest in medical training would be an asset. He planned to expand his office while I finished my Air Force service. And he'd get a fully detailed contract drawn up. Regardless of seniority, he said, as partners we should share work equally, and the contract should reflect that view. He wanted to alternate nights and weekends off, and he insisted that I attend my share of the medical conventions. As for our financial arrangement, I was to get 35 per cent of the partnership's net income the first year, with an increase of 5 percentage points each year until we were on a 50-50 basis. The contract also provided that either man could end the partnership on six months' notice.

When I was two weeks away from getting my Air Force release, Dr. Rainey sent his patients an announcement summarizing my qualifications and declaring his confidence in me. Then, during the first few weeks after I joined him, he introduced me enthusiastically to every patient who came in. I was embarrassed by the way he built me up, but the patients quickly felt at home with me, and our practice grew faster than I'd hoped.

Now Dr. Rainey and I are in our fourth year of partnership. Each year has brought us more patients, greater financial rewards and deeper professional satisfaction in working together. I'm glad I took the trouble to look long and hard for the right man. I've found him.

15.

We tested partnership while practicing apart

By Fred L. Evans, M.D.

When my two colleagues and I first started talking partnership, we certainly didn't contemplate a "trial marriage." Now, having had that experience, we wouldn't have done it any other way.

As internists in Chico, Calif., the three of us had growing solo practices in the same town. For a year we'd covered for each other on vacations and weekends. The trouble was that this coverage was not enough; we were still overworked. Finally, we realized that our practices were bursting at the seams; it was time for a more workable arrangement.

We considered two solutions. First, we could each take in an associate to absorb the overload. But since none of us had enough office space to house two doctors, all three of us would have had to move. The other possibility—form a partnership and move in together—seemed ideal. We liked the advantages a partnership would offer: time off, better facilities through the pooling of equipment, greater financial security, ease of consultation, etc. But again we ran into a snag. In our town there was no office space large enough to accommodate the three of us and our laboratory equipment.

Should we build our own office? We were leery. How could we be certain in advance that we'd be compatible? Since we'd have to set up a building-and-land corporation immediately, we'd be getting in so deep financially that there'd be no way out if we wanted out.

We decided to talk to a professional management consultant, Arthur Soderberg of Medical Management Control in Sacramento, Calif. He suggested that we form a true partnership and share income and expenses—but not practice together until we were certain we'd get along with each other. When that time came, he said, we could go ahead and start building our office.

This seemed sound advice, so we adopted Soderberg's plan and signed the partnership agreement our lawyers drew up. Then for a year we had the advantage of being "married" without facing the complications of unloading community property in case we got "divorced." If one of us wanted to quit, his only penalty would be the loss of his share of accounts receivable.

The trial period allowed us to observe each other's methods and professional personalities during our frequent business meetings. We also had time to adjust to the restrictions of a partnership. In solo practice we weren't accustomed to answering to anyone. For example, we'd go out and buy new equipment without hesitation. In a partnership, we had to wait and talk it over with each other. Annoying as this was at first, we gradually got used to sitting down and discussing such things. It was one of the ways we got to know each other better.

Was our partnership contract written to allow for the fact that we were practicing separately? Not at all. In fact, we didn't change it when we formed the building-and-land corporation a year later or when we moved into our new quarters six months after that.

Our income-sharing was and is on a percentage basis. As for overhead, we practiced as though we were in one building, lumping our rent and office expenses together and splitting the total across the board. We wanted no halfway measures. We figured the only way to see if a partnership would work was to practice as one in every way we could.

Until we moved into our new quarters, our statements went out from each individual office. The proceeds, of course, went into our partnership account. As soon as we purchased land, we sent announcements to all our patients, telling them we had associated ourselves so we could give them better diagnostic facilities, 24-hour coverage and, where desirable, the advantage of combined judgment in diagnosis and treatment. We also told them of the plans for our future office, which by that time had started to develop into a complete medical arts center.

We had no problems with the patients. Many commented favorably along these lines: "I see you've gone into partnership. That's fine. Now maybe you'll get some rest." A few seemed reluctant to go to the other partners. We assured them they wouldn't have to unless, of course, they became acutely ill when their own doctor was out of town. We pointed out the advantages of the other doctors' having access to their charts. They agreed.

Our partnership-apart really worked. By the time we were ready to build, we were also ready to invest our money in the project without the slightest qualms. That mutual certainty of success has since been justified. Our practices are still booming, and we're less harassed—knowing that our patients will be well cared for even when one of us isn't available.

16.

All my patients have two doctors

By Bertram B. Moss, M.D.

My last patient this afternoon was Mrs. Flanders. "Good-by, Dr. Barnett," she said as she left. She slipped out before I could correct her. Dr. Barnett is my partner, and I think Mrs. Flanders' little confusion is a tribute to our success in making our patients loyal to the partnership instead of to the doctor.

Dr. Barnett and I are G.P.s in Chicago. Each of us had been in solo practice a number of years when we decided to become partners. We agreed that one simple rule would govern this partnership: We'd share alike on everything—time, work, money, facilities and patients. And by sharing patients, I mean just that. Neither of us has a single patient of his own. And neither of us sees any of the partnership's patients more than twice in succession. After two visits—whether two days or two years later—the patient is seen by the other partner.

Our share-and-share-alike regimen doesn't end at 5:30 P.M.

either. That's when the system begins to benefit *us*. My partner and I alternate the "duty" on a 24-hour basis. So every other day I'm free of emergency calls, hospital rounds and being routed out of bed at night. And because each of us is familiar with each patient's recent medical history, there are no snags in this arrangement.

Here's another benefit: Our system allows us to do all the things physicians ought to be doing but often can't. We both have time for family life, organizational work and continuing our medical studies. For instance, last year I went to the A.A.G.P. meeting in Florida. So did a G.P.-friend of mine in solo practice. While I was free to stay nearly three full days, he didn't even get there until late the second evening. And by mid-afternoon the next day he was flying back to check on a hospitalized heart patient who was showing little faith in the physician my friend had gotten to cover for him.

There's more to our arrangement than just convenience for the physician. The patient stands to gain from it, too. When one of us is unavailable, no patient feels he's being forced to accept a substitute. If my partner goes to a three-day medical meeting in New York, our patients hardly realize he's gone. All they know is that this time they happened to be treated by me.

Patients also benefit when my partner and I consult each other —often in the patient's presence—on the more serious cases. The result is that the patient is aware we both have an intimate understanding of his problems—and is apt to think two heads are better than one. And the psychological uplift that comes from knowing there's an extra personal physician available in time of need is substantial. This is especially true with timid patients.

It's this kind of patient acceptance that keeps our system running smoothly. Most of our new patients are referred by others already sold on the plan. This means newcomers usually know something about our methods. So when either of us sees a new patient, he immediately introduces the other partner. Then together we explain our alternating system and stress its advantages for both our patients and ourselves.

Complaints? Sure, we've had them. And some patients have left us—but not many. Most of our troubles come from patients who develop a preference for one of us over the other. In the early days we occasionally yielded the point. But now we stand rock-firm for two reasons: We've found that one exception is apt to beget another. And it takes only a few such patients to rob the whole plan of its effectiveness.

Whenever I explain how our plan works to a colleague already in partnership, his first comment is usually, "It sounds great, but would it work for us?" I have to confess I don't know. I can only say that it's worked for my partner and me for 12 years.

17.

We can take a residency and keep our practice, too

By Walter Sage Ravenal, M.D.

I've been a G.P. for more than 20 years, but if I had my life to live over, I'd be an obstetrician today. I just happen to love that side of my work. And I know plenty of other G.P.s who wish they'd trained for a specialty—as well as a few specialists who wish they'd picked a different field of practice.

Wouldn't it be nice if each of us could practice a few years and then choose the specialty he knows he really enjoys? That's not such a far-out idea as you may think. True, once you've built up your practice and struck roots in your community, it isn't easy. But it can be done—even if you don't have a private income and nobody is offering you a grant.

My partners and I have proved it can be done. In fact, partnership is the key to the whole idea. If you're a solo practitioner, you might even consider going into a partnership as a means of reaching your specialty goal.

Back in 1959, we were a three-man partnership. My junior partners, Arthur Logan and Pete Saunders, were both 37. Each was a well-trained G.P. with about six years of private practice behind him. Though we were located in a town of barely 2,000 people, patients came to us from miles around because of the dearth of doctors in the area. We often treated as many as 100 a day at our clinic, and my two junior partners were netting $20,000 a year each before taxes.

The plan began to take shape when I realized that the special interests of my two young partners were right in line with the medical needs of our community. Arthur was a "think" man with a strong bent for internal medicine and a positive aversion to surgery. He often referred his surgical cases to Pete, who was delighted to have them. Pete's only regret was that he lacked the training to perform some of the more complicated procedures. He sometimes spoke wistfully of a concentrated course in advanced surgery at a distant university.

One day I took him up on it. "Look," I said at one of our regular luncheon meetings, "why don't you and Arthur both go back to school and become full-fledged specialists?"

They started to object at once, but I held up my hand. "I've thought it through," I told them. "I know you can't do it on your own, but as a group we can swing it. And think what it'll mean to our clinic to be able to offer specialized skills out here in the sticks! Instead of referring our patients to specialists 60 miles away, we'll be *getting* referrals from this whole area. On top of that, you won't have any worries about establishing a practice all over again when you come back—you won't lose your patients to outsiders while you're gone."

Arthur and Pete were excited about the idea. The only question was how their wives would feel about it. Each man had young children, and my plan would involve some financial sacrifice and dislocation. Yet both wives were not only game but eager to help their husbands realize a long-cherished dream.

Our plan was simple. First Pete and then Arthur would take a leave of absence without pay but with no loss of seniority. (In our group, pay is based strictly on seniority.) Each trainee would be aided by an interest-free loan from the remaining partners.

A permanent fourth partner, to be added immediately, would help the clinic maintain its normal patient load. By the time Pete and Arthur finished their training, this new partner might have decided on a specialty for himself. And by the time *he* returned from training, the group's practice might well have grown to the point where four men would be needed on the job.

We had no trouble finding a G.P. fresh out of the Army who was eager to join our group. Shortly afterward, Pete set out for his advanced training. Since the university he chose was 500 miles away and his children weren't in school yet, he took his whole family along.

Pete's financial problems were pretty complicated. He received no salary from the clinic during his 20 months at the university, and he could count on an income of only $500 a month. Of that, $400 was a loan from Arthur and me; the remaining $100 was the rental that our new junior partner had agreed to pay for the use of Pete's office and equipment.

The total, of course, didn't come anywhere near covering Pete's expenses. Tuition and related costs came to $1,500, and on top of that he had the expense of maintaining two homes. So Pete and his wife had to plow their savings under and then cash in their children's education insurance. (On his return to practice, we insisted that he replace that insurance before he began to repay our loan.)

After he wound up his university course, Pete's financial problem eased a bit. He moved his family back home and put in a year of residency at a metropolitan hospital 65 miles away. Since he could now commute home on weekends, he was able to work off some of his debt by doing surgery at the clinic on weekends. Today, Pete is back with us; he has a good load of major surgical cases and no regrets.

Arthur was the next to take specialty training. He set out for a two-year residency at the same hospital where Pete had taken his. His wife stayed behind with the two children, who were already in school, and Arthur commuted as Pete had done.

Arthur's financial problems were far less difficult than Pete's. In the time Pete had been away, Arthur had boosted his net income from $20,000 to nearly $25,000 a year. And his home and two cars were paid for. All in all, at the start of his venture he was in a sounder financial position than some young doctors might be. And although his income naturally suffered a sharp setback, he never had to use any of his savings.

Arthur figured his family's living expenses would average $600 a month over the two-year period. His residency would pay him $150 a month, while his investments would yield a further $50 or $60. Like Pete, he'd be getting that $100-a-month rental from our junior partner. The clinic lent him the remaining $300 a month the first year. In the second, he was able to earn this by helping our group on weekends—reading ECGs, serving as a consultant, etc.

One out of three G.P.s wishes he were a specialist

If you had it to do all over again, would you pick the same field of practice? MEDICAL ECONOMICS put that question to a cross section of doctors a few years ago. Here's how many said they'd choose a different field of practice:

Pediatricians	37%
G.P.s	34
Obstetricians	22
Surgeons	19
Internists	18
Psychiatrists	15

Both Arthur and Pete are now practicing mainly in their chosen fields. "Naturally," says Arthur, "there are times when I still have to sew up cut toes and banged heads. In a small town like this, where you're often the only doctor on call, you have to take it as it comes."

Both men agree that their prolonged absence cost them no patients to speak of. "I lost just three patients," says Pete, "and two of them were doctor-hopping even before they came to me."

Most of our patients, of course, are delighted to have treatment or consultation from well-trained men so readily available. New patients are coming in steadily—some on referral from their family doctors, some on the recommendation of other patients. All of us are enjoying larger incomes. Our group practice has already grown to the point where it keeps all four of us busy. Next time one of us wants to head out for advanced training, we'll need still another man to take up the slack.

When will that next time be? Our newest partner thinks advanced training is a great idea, but he says it will take him a while to pick his specialty. Meanwhile, the hospital people have approached me with the suggestion that I take an OBG residency.

When we started this plan five years ago, I felt I was too settled and too busy to go back into training myself. Now I'm not so sure. If it were just for the money, I'd say life's too short. But when I consider the adventure of going back to school after all these years, and the professional satisfaction within my grasp, life doesn't seem so short after all. Fact is, I'm seriously considering taking that residency.

18.

Solo practice or partnership? We've got the best of each!

By Emory Lipman George, M.D.

It's taken two decades, but I've finally found a practice arrangement that suits me perfectly. Though unusual, it has the benefits of a partnership without the conflicts and frustrations, and the independence of solo practice without the fatigue and financial insecurity. How did I wind up with the arrangement I've got? By trial and error.

I'd tried solo practice, two-man partnership, group partnership and expense-sharing before I hit on this new arrangement. It's something in between expense-sharing and full partnership. We call it an "association." And though each of those preceding set-ups had its advantages, all but the last had overriding drawbacks. Let me tell you my story:

I started practice as a solo G.P. 20 years ago in Ohio. My practice expanded rapidly, but the demands on my time were cutting away too much of my family life. So after seven years of overwork, when a fellow G.P. named Fred Noble suggested a 50-50 partnership, I jumped at the proposal.

At first our partnership sailed along smoothly. Patients liked Fred, and we were both equally productive. But he suffered from migraine attacks that progressively reduced his ability to work. Sometimes he'd leave me with a double patient load for days. In our fourth year together, it occurred to me that I was working more hours in partnership than I'd been working solo.

So Fred and I talked things over. We decided that we needed more manpower. Over the next few years we took in three more G.P.-partners, and the practice expanded accordingly. To keep pace, the five of us put up a new medical building with lab and X-ray facilities. Before long we were getting referrals from all over town for diagnostic workups. We were doing well.

But were we satisfied with the partnerships? We were not. Though each of us respected the professional abilities of the others, each had traits that were privately annoying. For instance, our third man, Vince Reddy, was overly generous with the partnership's drug supplies. Our fourth man, Dick Bostleman, developed a tiresome cockiness that quite a few patients disliked. For all that, both Vince and Dick were conscientious workers; each produced a fair share of the partnership's income.

I can't say the same for our fifth man, Frank Foldon. He was an ardent stock market speculator whose working hours were interrupted by long phone talks with his broker. In 1959, a totting-up showed that he'd produced only 15 per cent of the partnership's income, though we all shared equally in the partnership's profits. In contrast, each of the remaining four of us was bringing in his 20 per cent share or more.

For a while, we managed to keep all these gripes to ourselves. Then Fred Noble broke a leg—an incident that started a chain of events resulting in the breakup of our partnership.

The rest of us were resigned to covering for Fred when he had his migraine attacks. But when it came time to decide how much income the practice should pay him for the time he'd be out with his broken leg, our latent anger boiled over. As our partnership agreement hadn't set a disability-pay formula, we had to fix the payment by majority vote. The figure we settled on was far below what Fred had expected.

Angered, he contrasted his production record with Frank Foldon's. That set Frank off; he blamed his poor performance on my "dictatorial manner" and charged that I'd made too many decisions without consulting the group. When the others agreed, I got mad, too. I'd been making the business decisions only because nobody else would be bothered, I told them. Still more charges and countercharges flew, and we finally voted to dissolve the partnership.

No, we weren't to part company; we decided that we'd go it alone—together. Though each had lost patience with our partnership, none wanted to discard the group's reputation or cast aside our well-equipped building. By staying in the building we already owned and sharing expenses, we'd be able to hold on to our capital investment profitably. But the partnership, we decided, was to expire officially on Dec. 31, 1960.

After that date the five of us began sharing expenses but competing with each other. We soon found that we were friendlier as competitors than we'd been as partners. One reason was that each of us could now work as he pleased without affecting the others.

The arrangement gave all of us new incentive. Frank Foldon put in more hours. Dick Bostleman climbed down off his high horse and became much more pleasant to his patients. And Fred Noble, who'd often forgotten in the past, remembered to report his hospital services to the bookkeeper.

By curbing our bad traits, all of us were now earning larger net incomes, ranging from $24,000 to $32,000 a year. (We'd netted $22,500 each in the last year of our partnership.) Each man's share of the accounts receivable was based on what he had charged on his books each month. We all contributed equally each month for joint expenses—office purchases, maintenance and the salaries of a receptionist, phone operator, bookkeeper and supply nurse. Lab expenses, including the salaries of two technicians, were split in proportion to the amount of work done for each doctor.

Despite the advantages, it gradually became evident that our new setup had flaws. Every business procedure seemed to be multiplied by five. For instance, a separate set of books was kept for each doctor by his own nurse-secretary. Thus, the bookkeeper and her assistant, both of whom we shared, had to keep track of five sets of books, plus seven bank accounts—one account for each doctor, one for shared expenses and one for the lab. Further, there was really nobody in charge of our medical center. The girls directed their questions to whichever doctor was handy and so drew a mixture of conflicting answers.

Worse, our individualism began to show up in the lack of uniformity in our fees. Patients who'd seen several of us under our mutual coverage arrangement discovered that each of us had set different values on similar procedures. Fred charged $5 for an office visit with an injection, I charged $7, and Vince $8. The patient was billed on separate statements, separately mailed, a procedure that often confused the patients and delayed collections.

Worst of all, our expense-sharing arrangement offered none of the financial security we had enjoyed as partners. No longer were there provisions for disability, retirement, death or withdrawal from the group. Sure, we'd given up these things for the independence of nonpartnership practice—but wasn't it possible, we asked, to have the best of both arrangements? We agreed to put the question to a management consultant—Clayton L. Scroggins of Cincinnati.

Scroggins spent a day observing our practice and an evening talking it over with us. At last he said, "What you're asking for are the comforts of marriage plus the freedom of bachelorhood.

It's an unusual order, but it's the kind of practice many doctors are groping for." He agreed to tackle the problem.

Two immediate needs emerged from Scroggins' study: Someone in our group had to have authority, and someone had to be brought in to help us cope with our expanding practice. We agreed to look for a young G.P. with managerial talents who was qualified to meet both needs. As managing director, he'd be empowered to make decisions on all joint practice matters—subject to regular policy meetings attended by all six of us.

Within two weeks we'd found and signed our man, Lowell Taylor. He'd finished his internship and had headed a small Army hospital overseas. He was eager to join our group, where he could benefit by our reputation and use our overflow of patients to build his own practice. He bought into our accounts receivable, furniture, fixtures, building and equipment for a fixed amount suggested by Scroggins.

Next, the six of us signed an "agreement of association" which had been worked out by Scroggins. This document maintains each doctor's solo status as a competing practitioner, though it makes us "partners" up to a point. Most important, it provides for the group's continuity and assures security for the group's individual members.

Each of us shares in the profits of our combined practices in proportion to his gross income from patients. When one of us retires, it's anticipated that the rest will absorb his patient load. And the retired physician will keep 75 per cent of his equity in the accounts receivable for a full three years.

The same arrangement will hold if one of us moves or withdraws from practice for any other reason. In the event of death, the same equity will accrue to the widow. The doctor will also keep his equity for three years if he's disabled or goes into military service. And in either of those events, he'll return to a practice that's been kept intact by his colleagues.

What's the difference between our arrangement and a partner-

Three practice arrangements: How they differ

The author went through an unusual succession of practice arrangements before he finally found his ideal solution. This table shows the technical differences between the three main types of practice he's had experience with.

	Partnership	*Expense-sharing*	*Association*
Assets	All shared equally	Some shared equally, some not shared	Some shared equally, some not shared
Expenses	All shared equally	Some shared equally, some shared on the basis of use, some not shared	Some shared on the basis of each doctor's gross earnings, some not shared
Net income	Divided equally	Each doctor gets what he earns	Each doctor gets what he earns
Fees	Same for all doctors	Each doctor sets his own	Same for all doctors
Billing	Combined bill from group	Separate bill from each doctor	Combined bill coded for each doctor
Disability provisions	Yes	No	Yes
Death benefits	Yes	No	Yes
Retirement benefits	Yes	No	Yes
Provision for continuity of group	No	No	Yes
Obligation to cover for each other	Mandatory	None	None*
Records	Merged	Separate	Merged

*Each doctor is paid for any coverage he provides.

ship with the net income split on the basis of collections? Mainly, it's the way we *feel*. We're free of the obligations that a conventional partnership entails. When one of us covers for another, he does so voluntarily and gets paid for it. If one of us wants to take things easy, he can do so without feeling that he's shirking. And each of us is free to quit the group without legal encumbrances.

Along with our sense of freedom and our security, we enjoy a new efficiency. For instance:

¶ We have one bank account for the lot and one set of books.

¶ We all charge the same fees for the same services.

¶ We've discontinued the lab as a separate entity, though each doctor is still credited for his lab services. Lab profits are now added to the combined practice profits before they're split.

¶ We've acquired a $4,000 bookkeeping machine to simplify and speed the handling of our complex accounts and have hired a girl who's trained in operating the machine.

¶ Each family receives one bill coded for each doctor, regardless of how many members of the family have visited us during the month. Each bill is itemized, and our delinquent accounts are systematically tracked.

So we enjoy not only the economics and other benefits of solo practitioners who share expenses, but also the kind of security that's usually reserved for partnerships. The arrangement is working well in all respects. In fact, I see no reason why solo men in any given area can't get together and arrange the same benefits for themselves. By taking advantage of our trials and errors, they can discover how easy it is to be "partners" and still stay solo.

Index

Income *(cont.)*:
  solo practice, 8
  tax deduction splits, 57-58
  See also Accounts receivable; Fees;
    Salaries
Incompatibility, *see* Disputes;
    Personal relationships
Incorporation, 22, 104
Insurance, 23, 86, 100
  partner life, 48

Laboratories, 5, 86, 87, 91, 118
  association arrangement and, 123
  expense-sharing and, 120
Law:
  contract advice, 42*n*, 51, 63, 81,
    86, 95
  employment contract and, 16
  liability, 5, 6, 67-68, 69
  mandatory arbitration clauses and,
    64
  restrictive covenants and, 70-71
  See also Contracts
Location, *see* Community, The

Malpractice, 17
Mayo Clinic, 5
MEDICAL ECONOMICS' Continuing
    Survey, cited, 8
MEDICAL ECONOMICS' survey of field
    preferences, 114
Military service, 49, 97, 98, 101
Moonlighting, 66-67, 68, 118
Mortgages, 20
Narcotics, 10, 73, 80
Negligence, 6
Night calls, 90, 101, 108
Nurses, 3-4, 65-66

Offices, 5, 6, 7, 23
  dissolution of partnership and,
    75-76, 119
  expense-sharing contract on, 10, 12
  partner investment, 20, 21-22, 47, 121
  partner life insurance and, 48
  partnership expansion of, 86-87,
    90, 91, 95, 100, 118
  sales profits, 58-59
  separate, in partnership, 103-105

Patients:
  attitudes of, 8, 74, 83, 95, 99-100
  family account bookkeeping, 123
  partner, introduction to, 86-87, 94,
    101, 105
  partner work loads and, 98
  partnership dissolution and, 77-78
  retirement equity and, 121
  sharing of, 107-109
Personal relationships, 1-3, 4, 6-7
  association arrangement and, 123
  competition incentive and, 119
  disputes, 63-71, 73-81, 83-84, 118-119
  inter-family, 84, 87, 90, 94-95
  junior partner requirements, 97-101
  objectivity in approach to partner-
    ship, 91-94, 100-101
  shared patients and, 108-109
  trial period, 9-17
  See also Families of physicians
Personnel, 5, 11, 21
  expense-sharing arrangement and,
    12, 120
  office expansion and, 86-87, 95
  policy decisions concerning, 65-66,
    67, 74
  salaries, 3-4, 21, 23, 65-66
Policy decisions, 65-66, 67, 74, 119
  manager arrangement, 121
Practice:
  arrangements compared, 122 *(chart)*
  association vs. partnership, 117-123
  cooperative, 35
  equitable division of, 3, 5, 74, 98, 99
  ethical practice clauses, 80
  group vs. partnership, 1, 5
  income levels and, 39-40, 98
  pooling, 21, 107-109
  separate-office partnership, 103-105
  solo, 2-3, 8, 47, 83, 84-85, 108, 123
  trial period growth of, 29-31, 85,
    86-87
Profits, *see* Income

Records, 77-78, 92-93, 105, 108
  practice arrangements compared,
    122 *(chart)*
Retirement, 34, 45-47, 120
  association contract and, 121
  benefit limitations, 54-55
  notice of, 53, 55, 74-75, 101